"I could be a killer."

"I don't believe that," Cathy whispered confidently, not backing down from the decidedly ominous aura about him.

Travis got up and stalked slowly toward her, the lights throwing his face into shadow. For a moment she did become apprehensive, seeing something that quickly crept over his strong male features and then was gone. But it wasn't a threat of danger. "You should," he said roughly, a hand suddenly grabbing her chin.

Cathy didn't allow herself to gasp in surprise, although her dark eyes widened as she stared up at him and felt his hand tilt her head back.

"I could hurt you, Cathy."

She swallowed, and her lips parted to speak, but Travis lowered his head, his mouth instantly covering hers in a possession that was total and unexpected.

ANNE HENRY
is also the author
of these titles in
Love Affair

CHEROKEE SUMMER
THE GLORY RUN

Only with the Heart

SANDRA KITT

A Love Affair from
HARLEQUIN
London · Toronto · New York · Sydney

First published in Great Britain in 1986 by
Harlequin, 15–16 Brook's Mews, London W1A 1DR

© Anne Henry 1985

ISBN 0 373 50328 8

18-0586

Printed and bound in Great Britain by
Cox & Wyman Ltd, Reading

Chapter One

The rain left crazy spots and tracks on the windowpane, creating patterns and pictures far more interesting than the actual street scenes beyond it. After all, what could be said about a dreary rainy day? Actually, thought Cathy with a deep sigh, quite a bit. It washed away grime, freshened and nourished the flora and fauna and created a romantic atmosphere for walking or just spending lazy days at home. Poems and songs had been dedicated to rainy days. Cathy knew, because she herself had frequently conjured up such images, as befits a would-be writer. But for the moment her imagination had neither energy nor incentive for flights of fancy. It was busy convincing her that the fluttering in her stomach was all nerves and would soon go away.

The glass began to fog before Cathy's eyes again, and she used a thin finger to wipe away a circle clear enough to continue her study of water trails.

A door opened somewhere off to the side, and a tall, thin, middle-aged black woman wearing half-framed glasses walked out, reading several sheets of paper. By practice and familiarity she was able to sidestep others crossing her path until she stood scanning the five women waiting with varying degrees of anticipation for their individual names to be called.

But the woman called no one. She quickly and alertly looked over the occupants of the brightly lit room as she tried to guess the one most likely to match the information she held in her hands. Her eyes finally settled on a slight figure, drawn into herself, staring out the window at the miserable weather. The older woman noticed that the younger one had a crop of short curly dark hair that bunched fuller in front over her forehead and curled shorter around her neck. The nose was short and pert, and the mouth bow-shaped, with a full, soft bottom lip. The skin, normally smooth and clear, was now somewhat sallow under the harsh fluorescent lights.

"Catherine Donnelly?" The name was called, and the woman was not surprised when the curly dark head swung in her direction with startled, nearly black eyes. The brows were soft and straight and barely visible under the fringe of her hair. The jaw was somewhat square, giving the young woman a Madonna look—dreamy, delicate and feminine. "Will you come with me, please?" The woman smiled reassuringly and turned back to her office.

Cathy nodded briefly, looking bewildered and lost but gathering her raincoat and bag and moving to obey. The door was closed behind her, and she took the chair indicated. She sat quietly, with not exactly a worried expression but certainly expectant and curious. But just for the moment the curiosity was directed toward the woman sitting opposite her behind a desk whose top was neat and orderly, like the occupant.

The woman's long, thin face was a rich cocoa in color, with just a bit of lipstick and no other makeup. Her thick hair, almost jet black and without a hint of gray, was pulled back and up into a soft twisted bun. Her dress was a simple plaid shirtwaist. Cathy guessed her to be in her mid-fifties, but the woman's face was completely unlined and smooth, making it doubly hard to read an expression or determine feelings from her. Except for the older woman's mouth, which seemed always to hold a gentle curved smile, and her eyes, which were direct and alert.

The woman took her seat and let out a small sigh. She'd seen young people like Cathy Donnelly before. They came to her totally unprepared and unsuspecting. Over the past ten years she had gotten used to simply giving the information required of her as clearly and professionally as possible. She could be removed, impartial or uninvolved without being indifferent. But every now and then there was one who touched her strangely and made her want to be kinder still, more understanding, and to take whatever time was needed to be of help. She experienced that instinctive response now as she watched Catherine Donnelly, feeling the need to be maternal.

"I'm Elizabeth Harris. Sorry I kept you waiting so long."

The huge, appealing dark eyes were raised, and softened into a brief smile. "I didn't mind waiting. I'm glad you were able to see me without an appointment," Cathy said evenly, her voice calm and low, suggesting shyness. "I'm just surprised that the other doctor sent me to you."

Elizabeth Harris raised a brow but kept an otherwise neutral face. "You mean Dr. Bennett? He said you were a new patient." Elizabeth spread out a number of pages over her desk, assessing the best way to continue. "Of course, he didn't know all of your medical history. And he couldn't find anything wrong that he could help you with," she finished carefuly.

Cathy leaned forward a little from the edge of her chair and looked openly at Mrs. Harris. "But he examined me twice. If he couldn't find anything, why send me to you?"

Mrs. Harris clasped her hands together and rested them on her desk. She raised her brows at Cathy. "Well, you wouldn't want him to treat you for a broken foot if it was only an ingrown toenail," she said, her small smile broadening.

Cathy stared for a moment and then laughed softly.

"He just wants to make sure we've covered all possibilities. Why don't you tell me how you've been feeling lately. That way I can fill in the rest of my report and tell you the findings."

Cathy blinked and moistened her lips. She absently brushed aside a dangling curl from her vision and thought for a moment. She was feeling uncomfortable right now, the way she had for weeks. A cross between feeling hollow and feeling too full, as if she'd eaten a heavy meal, or nothing at all. A slim hand hugged around her midriff, and she thought with wry humor that if she was sick right now, Elizabeth Harris would have a firsthand opportunity to see her "illness" at work.

"Well, I started out just feeling very tired. I'd come home at night and go right to bed and sleep straight through until the next morning. But then all the next day I'd still be tired."

"What kind of work do you do?" Elizabeth interrupted.

"I'm an assistant editor with a small publishing house." Cathy thought a second and raised a rueful brow. "That is, I used to be."

Mrs. Harris tilted her head inquiringly.

"I moved here recently from Baltimore. I'm taking a year off to work on a couple of books."

"Oh! Are you a writer, too?"

Cathy chuckled softly and shrugged. "I don't know yet. That's what I'm going to find out."

"The great American novel, I suppose?" Elizabeth asked with an understanding grin.

Cathy shook her head diffidently. "I doubt it. I don't think I have enough experience for that yet."

"Short stories, then?"

"Poetry..." Cathy corrected. "And some essays. But I often thought it would be fun to try children's stories."

"Do you mean that someday I'll be able to say I knew you when?" Elizabeth teased unexpectedly.

"I hope so." Cathy smiled, liking her more and more. But then she blinked and sobered, remembering the mission at hand. Elizabeth correctly read the change in her.

"And when did you start feeing tired so much of the time?" she asked, once more the interviewer.

"I guess...just about the time I was preparing to leave Baltimore. I'd say a month ago. I thought it was all the packing and arranging to move here or nerves from getting started in a new city."

"How long have you been in Florida?"

"Almost three weeks. I'm still settling in...and still feeling somewhat tired."

Elizabeth made a notation and scanned down a page. Cathy frowned and watched the scratching of the pencil over the paper in fascination, unconsciously gnawing the inside of her bottom lip.

"So you didn't see a doctor before leaving Batimore?"

Cathy just shook her head, the curls over her forehead swinging gently. "No...I didn't think it was necessary at the time. And I was so busy trying to get started and away, I didn't think about how I was feeling too much." Suddenly, Cathy smiled, and her face lost the Madonna softness and became momentarily impish. "And I was still trying to convince my—my family that I wasn't leaving them forever."

"Overprotective?" Eizabeth guessed, peering over her glasses.

"A little," Cathy admitted a bit dryly, leaving the details of her past existence unvoiced. Again her dark eyes became large and looked with appeal at Mrs. Harris.

"How else have you been feeling?" Elizabeth continued. Cathy grimaced.

"Sick to my stomach—no matter what I eat. And sometimes feeling tight here....." Cathy ran her hand over her midriff for emphasis. "Several times I've been dizzy, and—" She stopped, as if just talking about all the symptoms was making them all happen to her right now. She swallowed to keep the feeling down. It was several seconds before Elizabeth Harris lifted her head from the page she wrote on and looked at Cathy.

"Is that everything?"

There was silence as they looked speculatively at each other. Cathy tilted her head thoughtfully, and her probing dark eyes carefully scanned the other woman's face. "You know what's wrong, don't you?" she asked clearly as her stomach churned in apprehension.

Elizabeth Harris started to say something as she adjusted her glasses but she stopped to consider her words. "Well, there need not be anything, wrong necessarily..." she hedged.

"But you have found something," Cathy said in a thin, hollow voice.

Mrs. Harris sat back in her chair. "It would seem so, Cathy." Her tone was purely professional again, even as she knew an urge to reach for Cathy's hand and hold it as an anchor for her against the news.

Cathy waited silently.

"Preliminary test results show that you're almost eight weeks pregnant."

The words were now out, and Elizabeth Harris braced herself for the reaction. Usually there was at least surprise. Sometimes it was a confirmation of what had been suspected, anyway. Often it was glad news, sometimes not. Often there were tears of joy, or sorrow. Sometimes a brief gasp or scream for the same reasons. Elizabeth had a set way of continuing the interview, depending on the initial reaction, and she'd found that being prepared for anything made her better able to help. So she was now rather speechless to find Cathy ony staring blankly at her as if she had just gone completely crazy.

"P-pregnant?" The words were more or less breathed out, although there was hardly a sound. The color drained from Cathy's face.

Elizabeth merely nodded, her eyes locked intently to Cathy's.

"But that's—that's impossible!"

Elizabeth looked down at the papers before her. How often had she heard that? Amazement...shock...denials. But the facts could not be falsified. The truth of so many findings said so. But for just a brief second she weakened. She was tempted to doubt herself, perhaps because Cathy Donnelly seemed so sure. Admittedly, there had been some false alarms over the years, but not many.

"Why do you say it's impossible?"

"Because I can't get pregnant!"

"You mean, this is a bad time for it to happen?"

"No, I mean it's not supposed to happen—ever. I've known since I was fourteen years old."

Now it was Elizabeth's turn to experience the shock that engulfed Cathy. None of it showed on her smooth brown face, however, other than a small curious frown. "What happened when you were fourteen?"

Absently, Cathy swept a hand over her curly hair, but it all sprang instantly back into place. "I—I had appendicitis. It ruptured. I had an infection, and there was damage to other organs. I was told that—that I'd probably never be able to conceive...." Her voice trailed off.

"Probably..." Elizabeth grabbed hold of the word. "But not absolutely."

Cathy stared at her, perplexed. "But I've never had cause to doubt that."

"You mean, you've never used any protection?" Elizabeth guessed with raised brows.

Cathy blinked but met the look without quavering. "No, I didn't. But I—I've never had to."

After a long moment, Elizabeth understood fully. She pursed her lips thoughtfully. This was much more complicated than she'd ever imagined it would be. Everything that had happened to Catherine Donnelly in the last two months was totally new and, Elizabeth would guess further, unexpected. Cathy was unprepared for the realities that now faced her.

Elizabeth asked Cathy about her last internal examination and was informed it was just a routine checkup done eight months ago.

"Why didn't the doctor tell me that the damage wasn't permanent?"

"He very likely wasn't looking for something as unusual as your problem." Elizabeth hesitated. "And as crazy as it sounds right now, getting pregnant was probably the only way you were going to find out you could! It's true that scarring from a rupture or infection happens. But the damage can't always be determined as permanent. At fourteen you hadn't finished developing or growing yet. How old are you now? Twenty-six? All these years your body has been changing."

Cathy squeezed her eyes closed for a moment and began to breathe deeply, as if to control some emotion suddenly bubbling up inside her. Elizabeth again felt the need to reach out to her, but she didn't. Not yet. For all her frail soft looks, Cathy Donnelly had her own strengths, and she was trying to use them now.

"And...you're sure?" she asked in a low whisper, words almost lost against the steady sound of rain on the office window. Elizabeth nodded.

"Almost positive," she responded gently. "But as I said, it's only a preliminary test. There are several others we'll have to do, plus a complete medical workup on you.''

The voice went on and on—gently, it was true, but right out of Cathy's head. At the moment there was a buzzing sensation and a sense of being separated from the whole situation—almost separated from her body. Someone had just told her she was going to have a baby. She was no longer just Catherine Donnelly from Baltimore, Maryland, who had dreams and plans for her life and even someone picked out who was to share it with her. She was now someone else, and other decisions had been made for her. Suddenly, all the rules were changed.

For twenty-six years she'd been protected and cared for under the loving auspices of her retired professor father and an older brother—six years longer than she would have liked. For twenty-six years she'd lived a fantasy life that was safe and secular but that gave her no chance to be herself, whatever that might be. There was a whole world outside of her family totally unexplored that held wonder and freedom. And there was Brian, who'd always been part of the packaged program, who was safe and predictable. He would treat her well and take further care of her. She would be acceptable and above reproach as the wife of a promising young lawyer hoping for a political career—as soon as she worked out the absurd need to be independent and creative and find herself.

Brian had been respectable, and respectful. With him she dared not explore that hazy side of their relationship that often called for her to sample the curious sensual warmth between them. It had never been permitted to blossom into full tantalizing heat. The curiosity was to be assuaged by someone else....

The buzzing grew louder in Cathy's ears. Goose bumps rose to life on her skin, but inside she felt hot, as if she were suffocating. The room began to tilt. Maybe if she just closed her eyes for a second, she could go back to being who she was before....

CATHY HAD BEEN OUT for no real time at all. She'd almost fainted, falling forward and reaching out for the edge of the desk. Elizabeth got her into another room and had her recline on a soft leather lounger. She was there holding Cathy's hand and smoothing away the curls from her damp forehead when Cathy blinked open her eyes mere moments later.

Elizabeth Harris looked different to her. First of all, the glasses were gone. Second, her voice had changed. Cathy warmed to the concerned murmurings and gentle squeezing of her fingers.

"You'll be fine. Just one shock too many."

"I suppose," Cathy said blankly, rubbing shaking fingers across her forehead. She wondered for an absurd moment what Elizabeth Harris's reaction would be to her throwing herself against her and crying her eyes out.

Oddly enough, Elizabeth was expecting it. But it never happened. Again some resolve and untutored strength came to Cathy's rescue. Grimacing as a wave of nausea swept over her, Cathy struggled into an upright position, swinging her slender legs to the floor.

"Not so fast!" Elizabeth admonished, but the gentleness remained in place, and her hold on Cathy's cool limp hand was firm.

"I—I don't think I've ever fainted before."

"Well, I have to admit it's not my first time seeing anyone almost faint at the news of being pregnant."

Cathy made no response to that, although her hand suddenly clutched tightly to Elizabeth's.

"Cathy, do you want to—to talk about this?" Elizabeth ventured softly.

There was no answer.

"Look...I realize from what you've told me that this is a tremendous shock to you." Her voice dropped lower, and her probing was very cautious. "If you're not married or committed to anyone—"

Cathy gently extracted her hand. She stood up and unsteadily made her way to a window, once more taking up her earlier absorption with the rain on the window. *Committed to anyone.* The words floated through her brain. *How do you define committment? Is it established over a long time, or do a few incredible hours count, as well?* "There's no one," she finally responded firmly, a sad finality to the hollow sound.

Cathy thought of her recently deceased father and her older brother, Chad, back in Baltimore. She thought of Brian. For no reason at all she thought of her mother, who'd been dead since before her second birthday. And she thought of a man named Travis.

At once there was a knotting in her stomach as a dark head took form in her vision—a sculptured face with a Greek profile out of myth and legend.

Elizabeth wanted to ask about the man involved, but didn't. Maybe he wasn't really involved but had simply been there, a physical partner toward a physical end with nothing in between. When Cathy turned back to face Elizabeth, she was calm again. Two bright spots of color were high on her cheeks, giving her a doll-like appearance. Her eyes seemed very bright and wide, and she smiled at the other woman.

"I'm all right," she murmured softly.

Elizabeth wasn't entirely convinced. "Are you sure?"

Cathy nodded, pressing her hand once more to her stomach.

"Then if you're feeling up to it, I'd like to finish the examination."

"Fine..." Cathy agreed vaguely, still stunned into momentary indifference. She allowed herself to be put through several more tests that afternoon until, almost prophetically, it was all over just as the rain was stopping. She filled out forms and answered questions and responded to directions automatically while her mind struggled to understand the significance of that day's news.

There was a great and lengthy discussion about the diagnosis at fourteen, and Cathy was asked to have medical records forwarded if she could. She nodded absently in consent, but there had never really been any doubt. The tests were all conclusive and in agreement with the first findings. She was pregnant.

When Cathy was dressed again and once more seated in Elizabeth's office, she was starting to feel as if she'd known the older woman a long time. Cathy had never had many female friends, having spent most of her life surrounded by men: her father and his colleagues, her brother and his friends. Cathy wondered if Elizabeth Harris had daughters of her own.

Like a camera scanning a row of faces, Cathy's mind came back to that of her mother, and she wondered about her suddenly. There were pictures of her, of course. The house had been filled with them, since her father had never remarried and had continued to raise his children in the house where he'd begun his married life. There were wedding pictures. Then there were pictures of Sarah Donnelly first with Chad and then herself; both of the children with varying degrees of curly hair like their mother, although Chad's bordered on being blond.

Cathy's favorite picture was one of the whole family, with her mother holding her by a chubby hand just after she'd started walking. In that picture her mother was thin and frail-looking, always reminding Cathy, years after, of a sweet, serene angel. She had no feelings about her mother one way or the other beyond the fact of their relationship. And she didn't often think of her. Sarah Donnelly had given her life but had never been a part of it.

Whatever need Cathy may have felt for womanly advice and companionship or motherly attentions had been supplied by her paternal grandmother, who had always been willing to answer Cathy's questions. To some extent she'd instructed her granddaughter, even in those things that she obviously found unladylike or embarrassing. But Grandma Anna's ideas of being a girl, a teenager, a young woman, were decidedly dated and confusing. After some aborted attempts to explain male-female relationships, Cathy had resorted to a good book from the library, gossip with school friends who knew as little as she, and eventually her own incomplete experience of trial and error—mostly resulting in more confusion.

All of this ran through her head as she felt lost—and lacking. And it seemed doubly strange that Elizabeth Harris, someone she'd met only a few hours ago, was the only one at hand to give her back a sense of clarity and help her through the emotional upheaval.

"One of the things we haven't talked about is what you want to do now," Elizabeth said gently.

Cathy gave her a sad smile. "Go on with my life."

"Well, of course. Eventually you'll go on. But what about right now?"

Cathy frowned. Her mind still had not gotten her beyond the bare facts of being pregnant. She had not thought to put it into the context of her life—what it meant for the next seven months, how it affected her staying in Florida, what it might mean two years from now. She wasn't blocking out the realities; they simply hadn't occurred to her.

It was like a denial, Eizabeth saw as she scanned the small pale face. Today some unexpected truths had been presented her, but tomorrow would be another day to go on with her life. But it had not fully hit her that her life was not going to be the same ever again.

"What are the choices?"

Elizabeth leaned forward a little across the desk. "Go on with your life—with or without the baby."

There was a long silence as the two women looked at each other.

"What...do you mean?" Cathy asked, although she knew. She watched as Elizabeth pursed her lips thoughtfully and tilted her head.

"You could have the baby. Obviously, because of that earlier medical problem, you'd have to be watched very closely, but very likely you could bring the baby to full term with minimum trouble.

"You could decide to have the baby and put it up for adoption if you felt you couldn't raise it—or didn't want to."

Cathy swallowed convulsively as the choices were laid out before her.

"Or—" Elizabeth held her gaze. "—you could decide to do neither, but to terminate the pregnancy."

"You mean...an abortion?" Cathy murmured.

"Yes."

The color drained from Cathy's face again, her cold hands clasped together. She'd never thought, in her whole adult life, that she'd have to consider having a baby. Suddenly, in one afternoon, the fact was that she was going to have one, and now she had also to consider if she wanted to have it or not.

"Cathy, I realize you've been hit with a lot of information today. In fact, it's been overwhelming. But it's better that you know everything now. There's a lot to think about and a lot to consider. You may want to talk to friends and family, although whatever decision you make must be your own." Elizabeth smiled kindly at her. "You may just want to be left alone for a while."

Yes. She wanted to be left alone. She needed some time to reorient herself and find her footing. She needed some time to go over it all again in her head. She wanted some time to cry...

"Here are my office and home numbers." Elizabeth scribbled them down and passed the paper to her. "I hope you'll call me if you have any questions. Or even if you just want to talk."

Time to be scared and time to feel...

"Will you go back to Baltimore?" Elizabeth asked.

"No, I don't think so." *I may never go back again,* Cathy thought frantically. "I'm going to stay here. There are things I had planned to do, and I want to try to do them, anyway," she said with determination, although her voice was thin.

"Then if you're going to stay, remember that there's help here if you need it. And a friend?" the other woman whispered earnestly.

Time to decide what to do—how to go on...

And, of course, there was Travis to be considered, although she had not seen him in two months. She had thought of him often but had not expected ever to see him again.

Chapter Two

The rain continued to fall, and all alone in a quiet corner of a local café, Cathy was once more staring out a rain-streaked window. She had pulled her arms out of the sleeves of her raincoat, but it was pulled around her shoulders nonetheless for warmth.

Cathy blinked as the waitress set a cup of tea before her, and she smiled briefly in thanks as the woman turned away. It was almost five o'clock, and the air was thick and steamy, curling her dark locks even more over her head.

When she'd left the center moments ago, she found her legs unsteady and her stomach queasy. Realizing that she hadn't eaten a thing since the night before, she knew she'd never make it back to her apartment if she didn't get something inside herself quickly. But once seated in the cozy, almost deserted restaurant, Cathy's stomach protested violently at the mere thought of food. Ignoring for the moment Elizabeth's admonitions to eat something, Cathy cheated and just ordered tea.

The rest of her interview with Elizabeth Harris had been rather one-sided. Elizabeth did all the talking, informing, instructing and coaxing Cathy in what she should and shouldn't do, at least for the time being. She had given Cathy brochures and pamphlets, one in particular entitled *Becoming a Mother.* Cathy had stared at it weakly, fingering it before hastily stuffing it into her purse.

"The nausea shouldn't last too much longer," Elizabeth told her, misunderstanding the vague look on Cathy's pale face. "Just eat small meals throughout the day. In a few weeks the symptoms should be gone.''

Cathy merely nodded, not really listening. Other more abstract thoughts and concerns were performing in her mind, evoking not only certain feelings and emotions but also the name and face of a man who was still a mystery. A dark stranger who'd comforted her and kept her warm and made love to her one night when they were both feeling alone and needy and only had each other.

Cathy closed her eyes and clenched her hands together, a swirl of emotions twisting through her stomach, a memory of both recent pain and past pleasure.

"Are you feeling a bit dizzy, as well?" Elizabeth asked, touching her arm, her voice solicitous and personal.

Cathy nodded, but her head virtually swam with images of a sleek, sweat-drenched body in the dark pressed warmly to her own, stilling the quaking in them both. She had been made dizzy then, as well, but for entirely different reasons.

"That will stop along with the nausea, if not sooner."

Again Cathy nodded, gnawing her lip. She gathered her things and prepared to leave. Elizabeth watched her with concern but tried not to show it. She recognized that Cathy would need to talk. But she wasn't going to do so right now. She couldn't. There was a simmering of emotions inside her that were new, raw and frightening, building up to a boiling tempo. It would not bubble over now, but it would eventually.

"Where will you go now?" Elizabeth asked as they both stood up.

Cathy almost smiled, wondering if Elizabeth thought she was going to do something desperate and foolish when she left the center. "I—I'm feeling very tired again. I want to go home."

"Would you like someone to go with you?"

Then Cathy did smile. "No, thank you. That's not necessary." She put on her raincoat and buttoned it methodically; she put her shoulder bag over her arm.

Elizabeth walked her to the door, aware of Cathy's straight-backed posture, her raised rounded chin, proud and a bit determined, as if she'd just been given a difficult, serious problem to solve and knew that eventually she would.

"I'm sure you'll feel much better after a rest. And don't forget to eat something!" Elizabeth hesitated as she opened the door and held it for Cathy. "I'd—I would like to hear from you again in a few days."

Cathy looked puzzled at her, and Elizabeth smiled, shaking her head. "No more examinations for now. I just want to talk with you about the pregnancy and that old diagnosis given you years ago."

"If you like," Cathy murmured, visibly relaxing. She felt utterly exhausted, and very dispirited as well. A lump formed in her throat as sudden panic swept over her. She didn't want to leave but she knew she had to. Eizabeth Harris had only given her facts and information. But it was up to her alone to decide what to do with them.

Cathy whispered a hasty, breathless good-bye and left Elizabeth's office before she changed her mind, or lost control.

Having always believed that she would very likely never have children of her own, Cathy had not thought too much or too often about it. Her feelings at best had been conflicting. How should she have felt? What should she be feeling right now besides overwhelmed and desperate? She'd sometimes thought, philosophically, that it was just not meant to be, her becoming a mother and nurturing a child born of care and commitment between herself and someone she loved. Cathy imagined it might have been pleasant. It might have been an exciting experience. But she had never been one to foster continual regrets or speculations of what might have been. After all, life did not owe her motherhood. Perhaps it was just as well, then, that the man she'd chosen to consider marriage with had decided that in the busy career of a would-be politician children would be a hindrance rather than a blessing. At one time, that factor had made her decision to marry Brian easy. He did not mind that she might never have children for him.

But she was pregnant, and Brian was not responsible. Yet for whatever reason right now, Brian was not the foremost thought in her mind. She supposed that in a way she'd betrayed him both physically and emotionally. But Cathy felt a curious, inexplicable triumph in so doing that was hard to admit to and difficult to handle, and that underlined her present fright and confusion.

Was it okay to feel panic, fear, doubt and joy sweep through her in alternating patterns and degrees of intensity? They filled her and drained her, made her weak and supplied new strengths. Being pregnant had changed her life. It had changed the past, present and future.

But there was the equally powerful and undeniable fact that the man with whom she'd accomplished this miracle was little more than a stranger. Someone with sad, sea-swept eyes and terrorizing dreams. Someone at turns gentle and desperate, hard and unyielding, searching for freedom from some painful past. Could she have the baby of someone so lost and incomplete? Could she have the baby for just herself when she felt the very same way?

Cathy wrapped her hands around the sturdy bowl of her tea mug and raised the steaming liquid to her mouth. She took a careful sip and could feel at once the warm trailing of the tea downward into her stomach. A kind of settling sensation took place, easing the odd hollowness inside she'd had all day. She was curious as to whether it was just the tea or the other physical change going on. Was she supposed to be able to tell? Should she be able to feel that there was something inside?

Cathy put the cup down and pulled the coat around her. Her eyes, dark and weary with fatigue, both physical and emotional, focused on the rain. She sighed. Why was it that all the most momentous events in her life recently had taken place in the rain? She closed her eyes and saw another rainy day, but it was two months earlier. That's when she first met Travis and thought him a god from the sea.

IT WAS JUST AFTER she'd won a heated argument with Brian and her brother, Chad, that she needed some time to herself. Her widowed father had recently passed away after a short but intense illness. From the time she was nineteen until his death, Cathy had been daughter, housekeeper, nurse and companion. She'd loved him dearly, especially his sense of humor and his ability to downplay his illness. She admired his ability to teach, garnishing her own love of the written word through him. But concentrating on him had allowed her very little time for the normal pursuits of a young woman. And before she and Brian decided on any commitment, she wanted and deserved a chance to belong just to herself.

Unfortunately, Brian, not understanding what he called her adolescent need to get away, had, in arguing the point, only strengthened her determination to take a year off alone. And it was not as if Brian himself desperatey loved her and wanted her to stay near him. He just didn't think her behavior was proper.

So Cathy, at twenty-six, had left home in Baltimore to travel south to Florida. She'd subleased a partially furnished apartment near the University of Miami, only a few blocks from Biscayne Bay and the beach. She'd left samples of her writing with three local publishers, hoping for occasional free-lance work, and with an exhilarating sense of freedom had set off to explore the area.

Cathy had taken a predictable and understandable day trip down U.S.1 to Key West, because that was where Ernest Hemingway had spent eight years writing stories that were to become legend. There she expected to find her own magic and inspiration.

Key West was the end of the run, almost the end of the world. That's how the descriptive brochure had phrased it. It fascinated Cathy enough to want to see this phantom corner of the United States at the very tip of Florida. She caught a bus in Miami that took her through Florida's out islands, strips of sand where life was conducted at a slow and easy pace.

The trip from Miami on U.S.1 began discouragingly enough with a drizzle of rain. But Cathy didn't really notice, as she at once began to experience those things that made that part of the country unique. The scenery was almost all seascape, and spectacular. The water of the Atlantic stretched endlessly to the horizon like a rippled plain of gray silk. And above it the sky, also a mottled gray, like pearl or marble.

On the bus Cathy pulled out an ever-present notepad and absently began writing brief descriptive phrases and words, trying to catch the sense of isolation and edge-of-the-world sensation she had looking out to sea. It was not a good day weatherwise for touring, but it was a good day for seeing the world at its most real and stark existence. Cathy declined the organized tour on the Key West Conch train and opted for exploring on her own. The town was an odd slapdash mixture of very old and almost new. It smelled of the history of Spanish sailors come to shore, of sunken ships off the point loaded with treasure and contraband, lost in the sea forever. It smelled of fish and salt air.

The architecture was highly individual, ranging from the stately and ornate to ramshackle cottages with dry, rotted, bleached wooden sides and roofs. There were seedy little side streets and dank alleys and a constant assortment of local personalities that gave the town so much color.

It was not her kind of world, Cathy decided, but it was easy to see the appeal, the raw, naked fascination this bare-bones kind of existence could have for a writer or artist. She lost track of time, because in this spot it was insignificant. Tomorrow was going to be the same as today. Unpretentious but easy. It was a wonderful place to hide or be lost in.

It was only by luck that Cathy found herself on Malloy Square at just the time of sunset. The street was crowded with the local Conch residents, tourists and those taking advantage of the large gathering of people to hawk their wares, including a man of indistinguishable age selling delicious, aromatic slices of banana bread. It was a magnificent occasion, to watch the orange-tinted ball that was the sun touch the edge of the water with light and melt its warm color into the surface, spreading it out like a fine wash of paint. Cathy's imaginative eyes and ears caught it all within and hoped that she could remember it later to put on paper.

And then, just as the sun slid below the horizon, Cathy realized that night was approaching in a strange city that had now gone almost dismal without the dressing of daylight. Having wandered so far and wide in the town, she was now also no longer sure where to catch her bus back to Miami. Cathy tried to retrace her steps, but it began to rain, hard and sudden, the way summer storms do. She hurried, but with each step the rain seemed to fall with more force until to continue meant getting completely soaked. She could feel water sloshing over the sides of her low-heeled leather shoes, immediately dampening her feet and making them cold. The short outcropping of weatherworn awnings on one narrow side street was not going to protect her adequately for much longer, and she felt the water begin to seep through her clothing.

Searching frantically along the deserted street, Cathy finally settled on the dubious interior of a tavern, as opposed to getting wet to the skin. Inside it was small but much nicer than the outside would have led one to imagine. It was dimly lit with old-fashioned kerosene lamps. There was sawdust on the floor, and the air was a musky faint combination of warm beer, the sea and sailors. There was a length of bar occupied by three men hunched over drinks. There were several small tables covered in brown-and-white-checkered vinyl tablecloths. One held two men talking in low, intense voices. At another table sat one lone man who couldn't have come in much before Cathy, since his yellow slicker was shiny and dripping with water.

Except for the man in the yellow slicker, all heads turned at her entrance. But the interest in her was desultory, and they all immediately went back to their private conversations.

Cathy hesitated for a moment, wondering if it was best to take her chances in the rain and try to find transportation back to the Miami area. She glanced at her watch, and seeing that it was almost seven, had a sick feeling in her stomach that she'd probably missed the bus. Cathy moved to the unoccupied end of the bar and stood waiting silently, beginning to feel uncomfortable in her damp, chilled clothing and in such an obviously manly enclave.

The bartender, finally noticing her, indifferently made his way the length of the counter, wiping with a sponge its already-spotless surface.

"What'll it be, lady?" he asked.

Cathy looked wide-eyed and uncertain at him, and he grinned knowingly, seeing that she was obviously lost and very out of place.

"I'd like to know where I can catch the bus back to Miami," Cathy asked evenly, trying to keep herself calm and unconcerned.

"You can catch it three blocks up on the other side of Duval."

"Thank you." Cathy sighed gratefully, turning away.

"But not until tomorrow."

She stopped and stared at him. Her curly hair was beginning to go limp, and several large loops corkscrewed over her forehead in front of her large sable eyes. "What..."

"I said you'll have to wait till tomorrow. The last bus to Miami left more than two hours ago."

"But...I came with that bus. I was supposed to go back with it!"

He chuckled dryly and without much sympathy for her situation. "Not tonight you won't!"

"Is there any other way to get back tonight?" she questioned hurriedly.

He shrugged. "You could get a cab over to the airfield. Maybe you could catch a flight back. But you might as well wait till morning." The bartender walked away, leaving Cathy stunned and bewildered. She had no idea what she was to do now. She stood frowning, gnawing on her lip as she thought of the options.

The door opened again, and a burly giant of a man staggered in. He bellowed across the room as he closed the door against the driving rain.

"Made it back, Joe. It's bad out there. I nearly drowned walking the last two blocks!" He laughed uproariously at his own joke. "Hope you kept my beer cold!" He pulled off his hat and carelessly shook the water from it to the floor as he approached the bar. His gait was unsteady, indicating that he'd been drinking earlier. The bartender set a beer before him and continued on to Cathy, setting a steaming mug before her.

She looked up askance at the bartender, and he gave her another lopsided smile from his unconcerned face.

"It's on the house. That'll warm your insides while you decide what you're going to do." He walked away again before Cathy had a chance to thank him. She began to feel less panicky and slowly pulled the tall mug toward her.

There was a movement to her left, and a great shadow floated across the bar top, blocking out both light and the rest of the room from her view. Cathy swung her head and met the bleary, lecherous look of the man who'd just come in.

"You look like you could use a little company!" he slurred with a leer.

Cathy blinked and inched away from him. "No, thank you," she said politely, and turned to stare down into the mug, hoping he'd just go away.

"Ah, come on! I'll buy you a drink. Better'n that stuff Joe gave you." He grimaced with distaste at the hot liquid before her.

Cathy visibly drew herself together and looked directly at him with a stubbornly raised chin. "I'm not alone," she improvised, her apprehension nonetheless rising. She had no idea how to handle this man, who looked and smelled as if he lived at sea and only occasionally came to shore for whiskey and women.

"Oh, yeah?" he scoffed, not believing her for a minute. "Who you with, honey?"

But then an arm insinuated itself between Cathy and her burly admirer, and a large masculine hand picked up her mug from her limp fingers.

"Back off, Hudson. The lady's with me," a quiet but deeply masculine voice said.

Cathy's eyes widened to see the face of the man who'd spoken. It was the stranger in the yellow slicker. The burly man named Hudson also stared nonplussed for a moment. Then he blinked and narrowed his eyes suspiciously.

"She's with you?" Hudson asked in a thick, rough

tone. "I didn't see her come in here with you, Travis," he finished, ready to argue the point.

"You're drunk. How would you know?" came back the dry response.

Cathy found herself still staring at him, trying to see his face in the dim room. He was taller than she was by almost a head, but nowhere near as tall as the other man. Under his yellow slicker was visible a navy-blue turtleneck with a lighter blue work shirt buttoned over that. He seemed overdressed for the mild spring temperature. His hair was dark and parted somewhere off center. It lay shiny and damp at the moment, with some of it falling over his forehead. The rest waved back over his ears, winglike and somewhat long over the collar of his shirt. He hadn't shaved in several days, and it was hard to see the features or lines of his face clearly or to tell his age. His voice had been even, clear, strong and authoritative. But he looked almost as disreputable as Hudson.

"Ah, come on, Travis! At least introduce me. Who knows? She might decide she likes me better!" And with that Hudson again broke into a boisterous alcoholic laugh. His stale breath reeked in a wave past Cathy's nose and automatically she wrinkled it fastidiousy.

"Forget it!" Travis said, and he turned back to his table, taking Cathy's mug with him. He said nothing to her, and she stood a moment longer, blinking after his tall form.

"Sure I can't change your mind, sugar?" The warm breath assailed her senses again. Quickly deciding on the lesser of two evils, Cathy followed the yellow slicker, leaving Hudson laughing behind her.

Cathy stood hesitantly watching as Travis lowered himself to his chair with obvious weariness and took a long gulp of his own drink. Over the rim he raised his eyes and brows at her. Cathy saw that his eyes were an eerie, beautiful gray-green, like the sea. He looked at her as if he'd forgotten all about her in those quick minutes crossing the floor. Cathy found herself mildly annoyed.

"Sit down," he drawled. "You're supposed to be with

me, remember?'' He let out a sigh and ran his hand distractedly through his damp hair, further ignoring her.

Cathy sat down opposite him, noticing the brown nylon duffel under his seat, lumpy with its contents. From the looks of him and his fatigue Cathy decided he'd just returned from somewhere. Was he a sailor, too? She wondered if he, like Hudson, belonged in Key West. Cathy glanced at the bar toward the other man and found that he, too, had quickly dismissed her from his mind as he brooded over his beer and muttered to himself. It was a strange world she'd wandered into; she felt as if she was of no significance here. She took an absentminded sip of her drink and grimaced. It was very tart.

"It's not supposed to taste good." The deep voice broke the small, silent space around her.

Cathy looked up at Travis as he reached to pull a pack of cigarettes from his pocket. He stretched out a long taut leg and forced a hand into his jeans pocket, digging for matches.

"Joe calls it tea Tasmania," he mumbled, his lips clamped around the unlit cigarette. Cathy nodded in understanding. A match was struck and hissed into a short, quick flame as he lit the cigarette and took a deep drag. "Keeps you from getting a chill," he finished informing her.

Cathy watched surreptitiously as Travis slouched in his chair, his leg still stretched out in such a way that if she decided to get up, she'd have to step over him. He seemed physically worn out as he smoked his cigarette with closed eyes, once again forgetting her, leaving her to examine openly her erstwhile rescuer.

She felt a growing sensation of excitement as she sat opposite this man, with his slightly scruffy but very male appearance. The awful tea had warmed and relaxed Cathy's body and her mind, and with her usual tendency toward imaginative speculation, she guessed the man named Travis was some sort of modern-day adventurer from the sea. He could have sailed from Greece or Spain, although he was neither Greek nor Spanish.

Cathy tilted her head, warming to her subject. He did

have the appearance of a Mediterranean pirate, perhaps dealing in some unlawful trade, smuggling or black market.... Did he have his own ship and a crew of lost men?

Cathy forgot all about getting back to Miami, or even Baltimore, as she played out her fantasy. And it was a few seconds before she realized that Travis was studying her with equal directness through the slits of half-closed eyes, veiled behind a wavy screen of cigarette smoke.

"What are you doing here, anyway?" the deep voice asked quietly.

Cathy straightened in her chair and, having been caught staring, guiltily dropped her eyes to her cup. Travis drew on his cigarette, finishing it and putting it out in an ashtray.

"This isn't a place for a woman like you."

Her eyes lifted challengingly to his face. "What is that supposed to mean? A woman like me?"

Travis's eyes wandered lazily but with indifference over her body, huddled in her light jacket. He shrugged, looking over his shoulder to signal the bartender. "You look lost...and too innocent."

"Well, I'm not! Lost, I mean," Cathy said pertly. "I was just walking around, and it started raining—"

"At least you had enough sense to come in out of it," Travis murmured caustically, then turned to the approaching bartender. "Another one, Joe..." He turned back to her. "The only females who generally come in here are the tourists looking for atmosphere or the ones looking to be picked up by a sailor. Are you either of those?" he asked with a raised brow, but Cathy wasn't so sure he was teasing.

"No, I'm not. Which is just as well, since the atmosphere and the choices are so poor!"

"Your point!" He grinned good-naturedly. Accepting the fresh drink, he then silently toasted her. He lit another cigarette and looked more intently at her this time, his eyes taking in more of her, seeing the small face with its square jaw, the locks of softly curling hair and the enormous dark eyes like pools that you could fall into. He blinked and narrowed his eyes at her. "You still haven't told me what you're doing in Key West," he reminded her.

"I wanted—" Cathy began, and was suddenly stopped as a sharp ear-piercing crack of thunder rocked the air and seemingly the tavern. Instinctively, she raised her hands to her face, reaching to cover her ears, but stopped halfway through the motion as her frightened eyes caught sight of the curious, searching expression on Travis's face.

A warm rosy color infused Cathy's cheeks as she realized how foolish an old childhood fear must have made her look. To cover her reaction, she took another sip of the tea, swallowing this time with no response to the bitter taste. Travis merely sat quietly and waited, not having moved at all but now, for the first time, totally aware of her as he watched the fear slowly subside.

"I—I wanted to see what Key West was like. I've read a lot about it," Cathy managed in a soft voice, listening with half an ear for the thunder to continue.

"So...you're a tourist!"

"It's not a disease, you know," Cathy responded with a short chuckle, her voice getting stronger. "And I'm not a tourist. I'm a writer."

Travis groaned and shuddered, flicking his cigarette ash into the ashtray. "That's worse. Did you come looking for inspiration?"

"Perhaps," she admitted a bit defensively, because he'd come so close to the truth, but also not adding that she sought freedom and life, as well. His obvious cynicism wiped away any possibility in Cathy's mind that he really cared to know.

"And I suppose you want to be the female Hemingway. You're a little young yet. Life hasn't given you enough experience, love, hate or surprises."

Most of that was true. Cathy wrinkled her nose. "Hemingway is not one of my favorite writers."

"Who is, then?"

She shrugged a slender shoulder. "No one yet. I still have a lot of reading to do."

"I believe you really mean it! I bet you plan to work your way through the classics, A to Z!"

Cathy ignored his pointed sarcasm. "My favorite book so far is *The Little Prince*."

He shook his head and chuckled dryly. "May I ask why?"

"Because he was an explorer, and he could always see the things that were really important with his heart and not his eyes," Cathy admitted honestly.

There was a curious silence when she stopped talking, and for an off moment there was not another sound in the whole room. Cathy and Travis looked at each other, the one heart-stopping young, the other world-weary old. It was in their eyes, curiously locked to each other as the rain continued drearily outside.

"Do you have any idea how many would-be writers, artists, philosophers, loafers, come here supposedly for inspiration? There's no inspiration here. There's nothing here."

Cathy immediately grew defensive. "That's not true!" And when Travis raised an indolent brow at her zealous response, she lifted her rounded chin. "There's a lot of history and color here."

"That's true of Timbuktu, but would you want to live there?"

"Maybe...if I decided there was something to see and learn. And you wouldn't have to stay. You could always leave a place if you're not happy."

Travis scowled disagreeably at her, then back to the burning tip of his cigarette as if he saw some displeasing image or memory in its glowing light. "Another dreamy-eyed romantic..." he muttered darkly.

Cathy frowned at him, tilting her head curiously. "You don't seem to think much of tourists, writers or dreamy-eyed romantics."

"I don't! They all see and believe things that aren't really true."

"They have imagination!"

"Through rose-colored glasses..."

"Our eyes are sometimes blind...."

"They come here because they can't make it anywhere else. Things are so bad here, the life so grim, that there's no reason for them to give it up. They can be anything they want here and no one cares.'' His voice now had a far away, thoughtful quality to it . . . and sad.

Cathy frowned even more at his abrupt withdrawal, suddenly feeling that Travis might well be talking of himself, too. There was a painful edge to his words that could only have been personal. "Then . . . why are you here?"

"Me?" He shrugged at the question, putting out the half-smoked cigarette and lifting his glass. "I'm just trying to stay alive," he muttered, and quickly downed the rest of his drink.

He confused her with his odd combination of indifference, and deeper burning attachment to some raw emotion and feelings. She didn't know how to respond to it but felt a reluctance to leave him alone to his personal miseries. But Travis ordered yet another drink, and Cathy sensed correctly that he didn't need or want her sympathies or company that night. He only needed a few drinks to deal with whatever it was that filled his mind with dark thoughts.

As if suddenly remembering where she was and how she'd come to be there, Cathy finished her tea, grimacing one last time over the taste. But it did the trick, making her feel a little more able to deal with the problem at hand—getting back to Miami. And she also didn't want to watch the ugly, sad transformation that Travis would put himself through, becoming like the man Hudson. Cathy would much rather remember Travis as her romantic notion of a sailor pirate from across the sea.

"Well, I should get going," Cathy said with a curious lack of motivation. Travis looked up at her, his eyes a bit bleary and their true color clouded. Slowly, he brought his body up straight in his chair and leaned forward. Cathy stiffened in surprise as he reached to wrap a glossy lock of her hair around his index finger.

"And where is it you should be getting to?" he asked in a quiet drawl, the voice almost suggestive. With a chill of despair, Cathy knew he wasn't talking to her. He could have been talking to any available female now.

Disappointed, she sat back away from him, and the

silken strands of her hair were released. "I have to see if I can get back to Miami." She stopped talking as Travis's head began to shake negatively.

"You'll never be able to in this rain. You'd do better finding a hotel for the night, although you probably won't have much luck there, either, since this is peak tourist season."

"Thanks!" Cathy smiled sarcastically at his less-than-welcome news.

He pursed his lips. "Just thought I'd warn you."

"Well, I have to do something. I can't stay in this tavern all night."

"Joe wouldn't mind."

"But I would!"

Cathy stood up and gathered her jacket around her. She thankfully remembered a red bandanna in her purse and pulled it out to tie the folded triangle of it over her head. She looked once more at Travis, seated not much below her eye level. "I thank you for your help before."

He slouched in his chair again. "No problem. By the way, who was it I rescued?"

"My name's Cathy. Cathy Donnelly."

"Cathy. I used to know a Cathy once" was all he said absently.

"Good night," Cathy murmured, but he didn't respond, staring moodily into space and slowly turning his glass around and around on the tablecloth.

At the door Cathy could hear the rain falling in torrents. She opened the door a bit, felt the cool night air, and hunching her shoulders, quickly stepped outside. She could barely see for all the rain, but taking a deep breath, she headed in quick steps toward the main street two blocks north. Before she reached the corner, her shoes were completely wet, as was her hair through the thin red scarf. Beads of water began to trickle down her face. She could feel the tapping of raindrops on her back and knew it was just a matter of minutes before the wetness permeated the twill of her jacket to her pale yellow sweater and denim skirt beneath. Her legs were clammy and wet, and her nylons were plastered to the skin. Cathy knew she wasn't going to make it. She was never going to get back to Miami before tomorrow, just as Joe and Travis had informed her. Feeling suddenly very sorry for herself and very uncomfortable, she wondered what she was going to do.

Cathy pulled back into a doorway and huddled dismally while she considered her next move. For a frantic moment she wondered if the bartender Joe would indeed let her sit in his tavern through the night.

Off in the distance, but sounding to her ears as if it were right over her head, was another clap of thunder. Not nearly as earthshaking as the ones before, but enough to make Cathy push against her small hovel as if she hoped to be absorbed and hidden in the wooden structure away from the storm and her fear.

Somewhere down the block the door to the tavern opened and closed. A tremendous panic seized Cathy as she was positive it was Hudson coming after her. The long ominous shadow of the man was thrown in front of her on the slick sidewalk by a lamplight. It moved in her direction, easily finding her soaked shivering form. It was Travis, and Cathy's relief was so great she was momentarily speechless.

His brown duffel was hoisted on his shoulder, and the collar of his slicker was pulled up, half hiding his face. But he was bareheaded, the water streaming down his face and dripping from his nose and chin.

"You didn't get very far... and you're going the wrong way," Travis drawled in a slightly thick voice.

"I—I'm sure it will—will stop soon," Cathy chattered.

"No, it won't," he said positively. "Not till sometime tomorrow. Maybe not even then."

An audible moan of misery escaped Cathy. She was beginning to be very cold, and the rain had finally reached the rest of her clothing. She balanced like a child on one foot, as if to keep the other dry or warm or at least functioning.

"Well, you can't just stay out here," Travis said a touch impatiently. "Come on... you'll stay on the boat tonight."

Cathy's head jerked up, and her round eyes sparkled apprehensively in the dark. She didn't move, and she didn't answer him. Travis made half a move to turn away and then stopped to look back at her.

"I don't know about you, but I'm getting wet," he began roughly. "And if it'll make you feel better, you're not at all my type. Besides, I've had too much to drink, and I'm too damned tired to care!"

And then he did begin to walk away. Never once did he look back, assuring Cathy that it really didn't matter one way or another to him. Hesitating until she felt water drizzle into her collar and down her back, Cathy started out after him, hurrying to catch up, her shoes squishing water with each step she took.

Chapter Three

Cathy's feet and toes were numb by the time Travis, oblivious of the wet, finished his slow-paced walk, bringing them to the waterfront. Cathy guessed he must live temporarily on one of the many boats moored to the marina. Indeed, he did finally stop and jump casually onto the deck of a rather box-shaped structure that was bargelike and two-storied. That was all Cathy noticed or cared to, as her own acute discomfort and chattering teeth made her more concerned with just getting inside, out of the rain.

Travis fiddled with a lock and a heavy bar plate fastened across the entrance. Then, applying a little muscle, he pushed until the door scraped and creaked, sliding open to show a dark interior. Cathy followed close behind, shivering uncontrollably in her thoroughly wet clothing. Water dripped from every part of her. She clutched the jacket to her body, not because it provided warmth but because it gave her something to hold on to.

Cathy stopped immediately inside the door, because she suddenly couldn't see a thing and the space was thick with stale, closed-in air. She gasped, using both her nose and mouth to breathe. She could hear Travis moving about in the dark. He bumped against something, causing it to scrape on the floor, and he cursed through his teeth. Something else thumped to the floor, making Cathy jump, her eyes stretching wide in an effort to find Travis. But suddenly there was the sound of breakers being thrown, and the room slowly flickered into dim visibility from two low-ceiling fluorescent lights.

Cathy let her breath out now that she could see clearly

and orient herself to the space. It was narrow, long and somewhat low, the ceiling only inches above Travis's head. It was sparsely furnished beyond the sturdy built-in furniture of a moving craft, everything secured to the floor and walls. It had a stark, cold unhomey look. Temporary...incomplete.

Her eyes now adjusted, Cathy looked to the man before her. Because the ceiling was so low Travis suddenly seemed much taller and bigger than her first impression of him had allowed. The yellow of his slicker was so vibrant and bright that between it and the ceiling light Travis's head and face, looking scruffy and wet, was thrown into a curiously ominous shadow. She couldn't really see his eyes, just black sockets where they should be, giving him a dark and dangerous appearance.

They stood staring at each other, neither looking in the least appealing or interesting at the moment but each suddenly aware physically of the other. Cathy felt a thread of excitement and wonder snake through her. It was very much connected to the male presence standing so confidently opposite her. The way in which he looked at her made her curiously aware, not only of their differences but also of a heightened sense of her being female.

Cathy forced herself to think of Brian. Neat, handsome, meticulous Brian, whom she'd know for years and understood. Brian, who was orderly, predictable and not likely ever to be caught in any situation he couldn't control. But Brian became a mere vague thought hundreds of miles away and for the moment almost unreal. The man before her was real. Cathy unknowingly tilted her head to the side a little with a puzzled expression, wondering what Travis looked like under his beard. She blinked away the speculation when Travis took a determined step toward her.

"You'll have to get out of those wet clothes," he said in a deep, low drawl, the effects of the alcohol only slightly apparent.

Cathy inadvertently clutched her jacket tighter, keeping her eyes wide and riveted on Travis's every move. Her nostrils flared gently with the smell of their damp, humid bodies. Travis took another step, and Cathy watched as his hand came up. She heard his laughter as the hand moved past her head and slammed the door behind her.

Travis moved back into the room, shrugging off the wet slicker and reaching to open all the portholes and windows on both walls.

"I've been away, so it's a little stuffy in here," Travis explained, putting the slicker on a wall hook and kicking his duffel aside.

"I—I don't mind," Cathy murmured, still trying to control the chattering of her teeth. The shivering was turning into a steady trembling all over her body.

Travis turned to look at her with a raised brow. "That's good," he said, amusement in his voice. "Since you don't have much alternative."

Thinking that he was making fun of her predicament, Cathy stood straight and raised her chin haughtily. "I can always go—go back to the tavern. I wouldn't want to—to put you out or anything."

Travis flicked an uninterested look up and down her slight but wet body. "You could hardly 'put me out,' as you say. But be my guest if you want to go back to Joe's," he said, and began working on the buttons of his blue shirt while also pulling out of his boots, one foot braced against the other.

"You're not being very nice about it!" Cathy complained.

"You're here, aren't you? And I never said I was going to be nice!" The shirt was off and tossed into a corner. "And if you don't get out of those clothes, you may not live long enough to get back to Miami."

There could be no denying the wisdom of his advice, except she couldn't very well take off her clothes, since she had nothing else to put on. Nonetheless, Cathy nodded and let go of the death grip she had on her jacket. She slowly unbuttoned it with cold, stiff fingers and took it off, holding it as the water dripped from it to the floor. Travis stopped pulling his sweater from his jeans to look at her once more.

"Oh, hell!" he muttered through his teeth, and marched

over to her. With one hand he snatched the coat from her hand. With the other he grabbed her wrist and walked toward a dark open doorway in the fourth wall. Travis tossed her jacket over the slicker in passing and continued on to the next room through it in the dark into yet another, and switched on a light. He left her standing in the middle of the square room while he rummaged in a wall cabinet, slamming the door and digging in a bureau, all the time muttering expletives under his breath. He turned, straightened up and came back to her. "Here," he said, thrusting an armful of things at her, "get out of your clothes and get dry!" Then he pushed past her, closed a screen to the room and left her.

"Thank you," Cathy said in soft bewilderment, but there was no chance that he'd heard her.

Travis had given her two good-sized brown towels, although they were rather stiff and rough of texture. There was also a red T-shirt. Cathy held it up to find the word DIVE printed across the front in bold white letters. That was it. Nothing else to accompany the shirt.

A violent sneeze finally spurred her into action. Cathy removed the sodden bandanna, kicked off her waterlogged shoes and peeled off the panty hose. She then gratefully removed the sweater and skirt, her bra and panties. With a sigh of relief at having them off, Cathy began to use one of the towels to rub briskly her chilled body, raised all over with gooseflesh. The towel was harsh against her arms and legs, her torso and face, leaving her pink all over and her face flushed. But it felt wonderful to be dry.

Cathy shook out the T-shirt and slipped it over her head. She was surprised when it dropped, stopping above her knees by a good three inches. Travis was certainly taller than she, but this shirt had to belong to a much bigger man. Its length, however, made her feel a little better about not having anything else on under it. With the second towel Cathy rubbed away the excess water from her hair and wrapped it turban fashion around her head. She picked up the wet things from the floor and looked around for a place to hang them, but there was just a double bed, the bureau and cabinets.

Suddenly, the screen was jerked back, making her gasp with Travis's sudden reappearance. He had on fresh dry jeans, and a towel was draped around his neck, the ends resting on an otherwise-naked chest. His shiny dark hair was still ruffled from having been only partially toweled dry. There was a momentary surprised silence as they both stared before Travis was again the first to break it.

"Were you planning on just standing here all night?"

"Couldn't you knock or something?" Cathy asked breathlessly, her indignation not able to disguise the vulnerable position she found herself in. But Travis merely held the curtain aside, waiting for her to precede him into the lit front sector.

Cathy slowly did so, embarrassingly aware of having no clothes on under the T-shirt. She tried not to pull on the hem of the shirt, drawing attention to that fact. But she also forgot that it left a considerable length of her shapely legs exposed, and she couldn't ignore the direction of Travis's glance as a brow and the corner of his mouth lifted appreciatively. Travis then reached out and took the wet pile of clothing from her and nodded to the open room they'd first entered.

"There's a heater against that wall. Sit down while I hang these up."

"I can do that!" Cathy protested at once, trying to take them back, not wanting Travis to handle her intimate garments. But as if reading her thoughts, he grinned rather wickedly and moved deftly away.

"I don't mind."

Cathy had no choice but to give in. Sitting nervously on the edge of the chair, Cathy watched as piece by piece Travis held up her clothing and placed them on a collapsible clothing rack under one of the portholes. Her filmy little bra was more lace than anything, and she felt the color rush hotly to her cheeks as Travis took his time stretching it out and placing it over the rack. When it came to her panties, Cathy turned her head away, but now because of rather tantalizing imaginings going through her own mind.

"Nice," she heard Travis croon softly, his voice filled with amusement. "Very nice."

Cathy swung her head angrily back to him. "I'm sure this is not the first time that you've handled a woman's... clothing!"

Finished with his chore, Travis held on to the ends of his towel and moved toward the doorway of the still-darkened center space. "It's not... but it's the first time I didn't have the pleasure of removing them myself."

Cathy had no quick answer for him as he continued to gaze openly at her. His eyes dropped momentarily to her chest where the word DIVE undulated, giving definite form to her curved flesh. She became uncomfortable under his scrutiny and hugged her arms around her body. The protective move brought Travis back from his private reverie, and his expression once again became indifferent. He turned into the dark room.

"Coffee or tea?" he shouted out, turning on the light, which allowed Cathy to see that it was a galley, with another small closed space that she presumed to be the bathroom.

"Coffee," Cathy answered, remembering how her tea had been enhanced at the tavern. In the ensuing silence that followed while Travis was busy, Cathy looked around the room. Travis had hung up his own wet things and emptied his duffel. There was a rectangular table bolted to the floor near one wall, with cushioned benches on both long sides. On the table was his wallet, keys, loose change, several logbooks and a number of charts. Swinging her head the other way, Cathy noticed a foam-cushioned sofa built into the opposite wall just inside the entrance, now made up as a bed, with sheets and a light blanket. All at once the magnitude of what she was doing hit her. Despite the now-comfortable warmth of the room, Cathy paled and shook at the implications of her being there alone with Travis. She had a flashing image of her brother and what his reaction would have been to finding his baby sister preparing to spend the night with someone she'd met a few hours before in a bar. Just as quickly, her fear subsided. Cathy knew with a certainty that this stranger would do no harm to her. As a matter of fact, beyond baiting her with her obvious lack of experience, Travis didn't seem impressed with her at all. Cathy began to wonder exactly what kind of woman Travis was impressed or moved by.

The rain was still falling heavily outside, and there came the sudden distant sound of thunder. Cathy's body went rigid. The thunder came again, and she was on her feet, hugging her body for control. Travis came through the opening from the galley, holding two steaming mugs. He quizzically watched the wide-eyed expression on her face and silently motioned her back to her chair. Cathy let out a small sigh of relief at seeing him and did as he indicated. She sat on one side of the long table, and Travis sat opposite her.

"Drink this. It should put some color back into your cheeks." Travis took a deep gulping swallow, and Cathy did the same, nearly choking as she recognized at once that tart bitter taste of the drink she'd had at the tavern. Travis chuckled softly at her expression.

"What is this habit of putting liquor in tea or coffee?"

Travis shrugged. "It takes longer to get drunk this way" was his flip, indifferent remark. But his humor quickly faded and was replaced by a glassy-eyed stare that looked through Cathy and not at her. "And sometimes it makes it easier to sleep...easier to forget." Travis blinked and focused on her, arching a brow. "And puts one more in the mood—"

"I'm not seducible." Cathy said in what she hoped was a firm, self-possessed tone. Travis interpreted it differently.

"I know," Travis responded dryly. "You're armored to the teeth in innocence. Either that or sheer stupidity!" He put down his mug sharply on the tabletop, and lifting the towel onto his head, began a rough rubbing to dry his hair completely.

Cathy silently puzzled over his observation while idly sipping on the hot coffee. She wondered if she really seemed so transparent and young, to the point where no one took her seriously. She wondered if Travis thought her attractive at all. Cathy was beginning to get used to the taste of the coffee and began also to feel a kind of mellow lethargy seep into her pores and flow through her bones. With a kind of detached curiosity she watched the movement of Travis's arms and his chest as he continued drying his towel-covered head.

His torso showed a firm, hard, molded chest that was completely void of hair and smoothly muscled. He was not particularly broad in the shoulders, but he was lithe and well proportioned. His stomach was flat and also muscled, and his jeans, riding a little on his hips, indicated that he was lean and narrow there, as well. The muscles played and moved strongly in his arms as he worked his hands. He was beautifully conditioned, and Cathy wondered exactly what kind of work he did. He could be Odysseus or Jason of the Argonauts, thought Cathy rather dreamily. Maybe he was an explorer and adventurer... a conqueror of men and women.

Cathy then noticed that there was a brutal scar along the inside of his left forearm, and there was a subtle discoloration on the back of both hands and arms, as if he'd healed from third-degree burns. It made her curious.

There was another clap of thunder, this one much closer and more violent. Instantly, Cathy was out of her chair, her daydreams dissolving. She gasped as the hot coffee sloshed over the cup rim and onto her arm. Travis had stopped his movement to look up at her in surprise at her sudden moves. But before he could say anything to soothe her, the thunder came again. The cup slipped completely from Cathy's hand and landed on the wooden floor, spilling its contents all over her feet. This time she did cry out softly from the scorching heat. Travis was out of his seat, reaching for her.

"Hey," he began softly, "Take it easy!"

He tried to put his arms around her, but Cathy resisted in her fright, stepping to the side and pushing his arms away.

"It's all right," Travis tried to tell her, but the words were lost in yet another roar of sound.

Cathy was overcome and stood stone still. She was

aware of a hand touching her, pulling her gently. She allowed herself to be turned, and a pair of warm, strong arms slowly circled her. There were words, too, but she didn't understand them. She just let herself be surrounded by the reassuring presence pulling her to safety. And when the sounds came again, she gave herself up to the protective shield, burrowing her head into his chest.

Travis's bearded chin rested against her forehead, and Cathy's cheek was flat against his smooth chest, listening to his even, steady heartbeat. He wasn't the least afraid. He was so sure, so calm, while her heart pounded in her chest. Cathy wrapped her arms around his waist, and she held on to him as if her life depended on it.

Cathy had no idea how long they stood that way, but she became aware of other sensations now. Her firm, rounded breasts pressed against Travis. His arm rested low on her back, the fingers rubbing through the cotton T-shirt at her waist and hip. Her bare thighs pressed against the denim of his, and she knew that the T-shirt had risen up when her arms went around him.

"You picked a bad time to be in Florida," Travis said, gently rubbing his chin against her, his voice deep and crooning. "Florida summers are always stormy, and steamy. Sometimes I think that Florida sunshine is a complete myth!" he added dryly.

"I—I didn't know..." Cathy whispered into his chest, lulled by his closeness.

"Obviously not," he commented. "September through November are even worse. That's hurricane season down here. And don't you know you should do a checklist before you take a boat out to sea?"

Cathy frowned. "What?" she asked, not understanding the analogy.

Travis chuckled silently, his chest moving against her cheek. "Never mind."

Travis didn't move until Cathy was calm and she herself gently pulled away from him. She had always been embarrassed of her fear of violent storms. Although she'd been afraid since childhood, she had, fortunately not experienced many of them growing up in Baltimore. She hadn't realized that the terror of them would spring to life again in Florida, without the familiarity of friends and family, who understood. Still, there was Travis.

Cathy, her eyes lowered, turned away from him. Her turban wrap had worked its way loose, and she removed it from her head.

"I'm sorry," she whispered softly, her face flushed. "I—I've always been afraid—"

"There's no need to explain." Travis said, close behind her, a hand just briefly reaching out to pass over her hair, watching in fascination as the curls sprang back into place. "Everyone's afraid of something."

"The cup. Did I break the cup?"

"Forget the cup. It was meant to bounce on these floors."

Cathy made a feeble attempt to smile but gave it up and just swallowed away the rest of her trauma. Travis then made himself busy putting away his towel, picking up the cup and wiping the floor. A kind of body-shaking exhaustion, built primarily from recent adventures, made Cathy feel suddenly drained. She continued to stand in one spot, half expecting the thunder to continue, but it seemed to have finally stopped.

Cathy blinked as she realized Travis was standing in front of her. She looked up at him, her eyes dark and tired, the color high on just her cheeks at the moment. His expression was thoughtful, and all at once he seemed almost angry with her.

"I think we should go to bed."

Cathy just stared at him.

"We'll both feel better for a night's rest." Travis jerked his thumb over his shoulder. "You sleep in there. I'll sleep on the couch out here."

Cathy came back to life, letting out a breath of relief. "I can sleep on the couch. There's no reason to give up your—"

"Good night!" Travis interrupted firmly.

Feeling as if she were being punished, Cathy murmured good night in return and quietly left the room. In the back room she pulled back the covers on the double bed. The linens were a bit damp, but they were very clean and welcoming. The light went out in the front section and the galley. There were small movements until Travis settled down completely and all was quiet.

"Good night," Cathy said again softly into the dark space, but she only heard another shifting of Travis on the couch and no other response.

Cathy sighed, turned out the light and gingerly crawled into the bed. It troubled her that she was taking over his bed, but she also knew an instant and strong sense of intimacy, as if his having slept there in the past made them now connected in some personal way. The thought kept her stiffly awake until finally the soft but steady deep breathing of exhaustion coming from the front room told her Travis was asleep. Relaxing at last, she fell asleep, too.

Sometime in the night a sound reached Cathy through her sleep. It was not the rain but something less regular and more demanding. Cathy turned over but only heard the sounds more clearly. A sudden loud cry of anguish brought her eyes open and her head up as something hit the floor in the front room. But then it was quiet. After a second there was movement and the other sounds, but softer.

"Travis?" Cathy whispered softly, but got no answer. Just further movement. Cathy got out of bed and cautiously moved in the dark toward the front room. She held both hands out in front of her so as not to bump unexpectedly into a wall or furniture. As she approached the room, she thought she heard a moan. "Travis?" she tried again but still no answer.

In the dark Travis seemed to be fidgeting and twitching on the couch. There was another moan and a garble of unintelligible words. Cathy stood confused for a second before her concern drove her farther into the room to stand next to Travis, stretched out on the narrow, too-short couch. He lay on his back, his chest heaving in deep erratic breathing. Despite the slight chill of the night, his chest was glistening with sweat. His arms were bent stiffly at the elbow and held rigidly, his hands spread as if bracing against something. Travis's body was so taut that tendons and sinews stood out in his neck, wrists and forearms. Even his face was contorted, as if in unbelievable pain.

Immediately, Cathy was apprehensive, thinking that he was in pain. But it became obvious from his disjointed ranting that he was deep in the throes of a dream that was very real for him.

"Mitch! Hold on...I...I can't. Oh, no!" The words were almost sobbed. In any case, he was experiencing genuine anguish.

Cathy approached the couch and cautiously sat on its very edge. The floor at the foot of the couch was all wet, and she balanced there, with only her toes touching the floor. Cathy watched in fascination as Travis writhed with some inner agony, not sure what would happen if she tried to awaken him.

His hands were still held out from his body. Cathy slowly touched them and tried to bring them down to his side on the bed. He resisted for a moment, but then the arms relaxed and dropped heavily. All the while the unclear sounds and words were muttered and moaned.

"I can't, Mitch.... It's so hot...."

Without realizing it, Cathy began her own murmurings. But her voice was gentle, her tone understanding—comforting. "Travis," Cathy called in a whisper, trying to gain his attention and pull him back from his dark abyss.

"It's gonna blow!" he groaned. "Get out...get out!"

"Travis...shh!" Cathy's right hand automatically brushed the damp thick hair from his forehead, the other hand pressed to his hard chest as if to steady him.

Suddenly, Travis was completely awake and alert, half sitting up so quickly, Cathy gasped in alarm. He responded immediately like a predatory animal, grabbing Cathy's wrist in a painful hold that could have snapped the slender bone. Cathy sat still, her heart racing, waiting for him to recognize her and where he was. Perspiration gleamed all over his body. He might have been burning up in fever.

Cathy's eyes caught his wild look and held. Travis returned the look blankly, and she was not sure he was seeing her at all. "Travis, you're dreaming," she murmured, freeing her wrist. Once again she ventured to stroke his forehead clear of hair. "It's only a dream."

Travis let out a deep, stiff sigh; then, with another groan, he collapsed heavily back on the bed, breathing to gain control. He said nothing further, and after a few minutes the only sound was the rain.

Cathy put a hand back to his chest cautiously and felt the even, slow beat of his heart at normal rest. She began to stroke her hand up and down several times, gliding over the damp, smooth surface, wanting to soothe him and not leave him alone yet.

"I'm not a crocodile, you know," Travis suddenly rasped out drowsily in the dark, instantly stilling Cathy's hand. She quickly removed it. Travis rolled over onto his side, his back to her, and was again instantly, peacefully asleep.

After another minute Cathy got up and quietly made her way back to her own solitary bed. Between the sheets once more, she wondered with real concern and curiosity what nightmare rendered him such a terrible night. What was Travis afraid of?

Chapter Four

Cathy stretched luxuriously in the bed, rolling over onto her back and out of a dream about a dark hero with sea-lit eyes. She blinked open her own and stared at the ceiling. She was trying to keep the dream image sharp as an idea for a poem took form in her mind. It often happened that she'd wake up with a word, a phrase, an image, that evoked ideas to be written out. But this peculiar creative habit of hers meant leaving a pad and pencil by the bed to capture quickly the delicate threads of thought before they vanished.

Cathy reached to her left side, to the usual place of her nightstand, only to encounter a wall. Only then did she remember where she was. She sat up, looking around the small room, dim and gray in the morning light. Cathy climbed out of bed, covering herself with the blanket. She walked to a porthole opposite the bed, stepping into a puddle of very cold water, wondering how it got there. One look out the porthole showed her it was still raining, but without the torrential downpour of the previous night. Cathy groaned in frustration, wondering who in heaven ever thought of Florida as a sunny paradise. She'd seen almost nothing but rain since arriving in Miami.

Then Cathy gasped in panic as she also realized she wasn't in Miami but still in a worn-out gulf town on a houseboat belonging to a sailor. Or was he a sailor? What was he, really, beyond what her imagination made him?

Cathy quietly left her room and walked into the galley. The smell of freshly brewed coffee filled the air, and there was an already-used mug on the wooden counter. But the space was empty. Cathy continued on to the front room, and it, too, was deserted. She frowned at the rumpled coverings thrown back on the couch. Looking around further, she saw that the yellow slicker was gone from the rack, as were Travis's heavy boots. She wondered where he was as she pulled the blanket more securely around her and shivered with sudden cold and dampness.

Cathy turned her thoughts to getting dressed quickly as she began to feel the inadequacy of the oversized T-shirt and the blanket. But when she reached for her clothing on the rack, she found them almost as wet as they'd been the night before. Cathy's brow furrowed, and her lips parted in total bewilderment. Everything should have been dry by now. Apprehension made her shiver as she realized that she would still not be able to get back to Miami. At least not for another few hours while she tried to figure out a way to get her things dry.

At that moment there were heavy footsteps landing on the deck of the barge. In another instant the door slid open as Travis walked in, his arms loaded with a number of small packages. His slicker was shiny with water, as were his beard and dark hair. Cathy wondered irrelevantly why he had an aversion to wearing hats. Travis used his foot to close the door again and turned to face her.

He stood still, taking in the waif-like appearance of Cathy, with her tangle of curly hair and her toes peeking out from beneath a blanket wrapped around her but mostly dragging on the floor.

Cathy, despite her concern for her predicament, noticed at once that his eyes were clear and alert that morning. And it was evident from the slow, amused look he gave her from head to toe that his restless tossing of the night before was not foremost on his mind. She blushed under his steady gaze, not feeling any less naked just because only her toes were visible.

"They're still wet!" Cathy said in exasperation, looking wide-eyed at Travis.

His grin turned into a puzzled frown. "What's wet?"

"These!" Cathy held up the sweater and skirt, still sodden with water. "They're not even close to being dry."

Travis shifted a package from one arm to the other and took a few steps closer to her. He looked a little hesitantly at her things, then back to her. "Yeah, well... it's probably all my fault. I think I kicked the stand over in my sleep last night. The wind shifted, and rain came in the portholes."

It was a perfectly reasonable explanation. "Oh..." was all she could murmur helplessly. It reminded her of his awful night, and if he had kicked the rack over, he wasn't conscious of having done so. Nonetheless, feeling defeated and thwarted, Cathy lowered her arms limply at her sides now, and she let out a sigh as she wondered what on earth she was going to do all day while her clothes dried. She was also feeling, rather fatalistically, that they probably never would dry and she was going to be stuck and lost in Key West forever, just becoming another would-be writer forgotten by the world.

She was brought back from her romantic martyrdom by Travis's moving past her into the galley with his packages. Things were simply dropped on any available surface.

"Cheer up," he said over his shoulder nonchalantly to her. "It could be worse."

After draping the garments once more on the rack, Cathy bleakly followed Travis, flexing her already-cold toes as she inadvertently trailed into his wet footsteps. "I'd like you to tell me how it could be worse?"

Travis slowly gave her a brief up-and-down glance, and shrugged out of the slicker and tossed it to her suddenly. Cathy was forced to release her hold on the blanket, and it dropped to the floor as she caught the wet, cold jacket against her chest, gasping with the feel of it. Travis chuckled, seemingly indifferent to her as he began opening packages.

Cathy gave him a baleful look before flouncing away to the coatrack, momentarily forgetting her scanty attire. Unbeknownst to her, Travis's eyes followed the graceful movement of her lithe, barefoot body, again making note of her shapely legs.

Cathy quickly returned to retrieve her blanket. "You haven't answered me."

Travis raised questioning dark brows, his gray-green eyes attractive in his angular face. He pulled a bandanna from his pocket to wipe his face, and Cathy absently noted that it was her red kerchief. "What was the question?" Travis asked, tying the scarf rakishly around his neck.

Cathy sighed, struggling for patience, and asked more clearly, "How could it be worse than being here with no clothes?"

Travis leaned back against the counter and casually lit a cigarette, tilting his head as he exhaled. "You could be with someone else with no clothes."

"You mean...someone I don't even know?" Cathy mouthed in dumbfounded disgust.

"Exactly!"

Cathy raised her chin. "Well...maybe I'd rather. After all, you're a stranger."

"Would you?" he asked without a pause, looking at her intently.

Cathy started to answer back flippantly but couldn't, because she knew she would only be kidding herself. And strangely enough, she sensed that Travis would know, as well. "No..." she finally answered softly.

They stared at each other for a long silent moment while the distance that had existed between them, on his part due to tired indifference the night before and on her part to uncertainty, melted away. They were left with just each other in a situation they'd neither looked for nor planned on and, in different ways, were both unprepared to handle.

"Is there someone waiting for you back in Miami?" Travis broke the lengthening silence with the question, drawing deeply on his cigarette with seemingly casual interest.

Cathy blinked. "No. No one," she again answered honestly, and somewhere inside she experienced the liberating excitement of being able to say so. There was Brian, of course, but he was in Washington. And she never asked him whom he met when he was on the road for business. This was her adventure. Brian had nothing to do with it. They didn't belong to each other yet.

"Then you're in no particular hurry. Stay and have some lunch."

"Lunch?" she asked blankly.

Travis allowed his cigarette to dangle from the corner of his mouth as he turned to finish his unpacking. "It's nearly one o'clock. A little late for breakfast, wouldn't you say? I thought maybe you were going to spend the day in bed." He grinned wickedly at her. "All in all not a bad idea, but I've got some things to do. We don't seem to be getting any hot water."

Cathy leaned against the door frame, trying to manage the mass of the blanket around her. "Have—have you been up for a long time?"

There was a slight hesitation in his movements, barely discernible, before Travis answered. His bantering tone was gone. "Since about seven. I'm an early riser." The reply was short and crisp.

Cathy noticed the tightness but said nothing more. There was silence again as she stood watching his back, thinking about his dreams of the night before. She wondered if he planned on mentioning it... explaining it. He didn't.

"I don't recall that either of us had dinner last night. Are you hungry?" Travis suddenly asked briefly over his shoulder.

"Yes, I am!" Cathy agreed wholeheartedly.

"Can you cook?" Travis asked, pulling a pot out of a cabinet.

Remembering all the meals she'd cooked for her father and brother since she was nearly fourteen, Cathy laughed softly in amusement. "Of course I can cook!"

"Good. You can make the lunch," he said easily, and turned to face her once more. Cathy began to fume at his presumption as Travis stood with hands on his hips, surveying her from head to toe and frowning thoughtfully. "But first I guess I'd better get you something to wear. Too bad..." he murmured, tossing the finished cigarette butt out a porthole and stepping past her on his way to the room where she'd spent the night.

Cathy made a face at his retreating back but nonetheless

moved to the counter and poked with curiosity through the odd assortment of foodstuffs he'd purchased. In a minute Travis was returning to the galley.

"I think these might fit you," he said. Cathy turned to find him holding up a narrow, small pair of jeans. One knee had a rip in it, and a back pocket had been torn half off and flapped loosely, but they looked like her size. There was also a plaid shirt, a pair of socks and a red wool crewneck sweater a bit moth-eaten around the neck and sleeves. It was obvious that the clothing didn't belong to Travis, and they weren't women's clothing. But before Cathy could ask whom they did belong to, he spoke. "I suggest you put these on, I personally don't think they're as interesting as what you have on, but they will keep you warm."

"I'm surprised you noticed," Cathy said tartly, taking the things and reminded of his bare civility to her the previous night. Strangely, a muscle tensed in his jaw, and his eyes turned pure gray and very cold. Cathy was taken aback by the sudden anger in his face.

"How old are you, anyway?" he asked brusquely.

"I don't see that my age is relevant!" Cathy informed him haughtily.

"You damn well better believe it is!" Travis gritted out in a low, dangerous tone. "You don't look like you're old enough to even be out on your own. And I don't normally baby-sit young attractive females. Now get dressed, for heaven's sake!"

Cathy stared at him, wondering about his sudden mood swing. Then the look in his face and the way his eyes flickered from her T-shirt-clad body alerted her to the possible cause. Cathy tilted her curly head in curiosity. "I thought you said I wasn't your type?"

"You're not," Travis said sharply, "but you happen to be here now!"

Travis moved swiftly past her, and grabbing his slicker once more, slammed out of the craft, leaving Cathy in the galley doorway, her cheeks flaming red. Cathy turned and stared after him long after he'd gone. She sensed, suddenly, that she was playing a dangerous game with Travis, even if unwittingly. He could hardly have made it plainer that he wasn't a man one flirted with, and certainly not without consequences. Cathy allowed her imagination to form one or two in her mind as she walked back to her temporary room to get dressed.

Without benefit of underwear, she dressed in the borrowed clothing; the jeans were snug around the hips and a little long in the legs but otherwise fit. The shirt was also a little tight across her chest, flattening her breasts. When she had everything on, she fluffed her hair with her fingers and went to make lunch.

It was obvious from the haphazard items that he simply shopped because he was hungry, and there wasn't much sense to what he purchased. There was fruit, bread, cheese, eggs, spaghetti, milk, soup, lettuce and bacon. Cathy quickly decided that grilled cheese sandwiches, soup and salad would do. After twenty minutes, when he still hadn't returned, she wrapped the sandwiches in foil, keeping them warm in a counter toaster oven. Then, with nothing else to do, Cathy folded away the linens on the narrow couch and casually looked around the space that Travis very likely called home.

It was bare. Stark. It had only the essentials for surviving at least decently. It was comfortable but not cozy. It didn't look like a place someone would live in, because it seemed so temporary. There were no personal things like a favorite chair or pictures on the paneled walls. No photographs or mementos as reminders of people, places or things. No books other than a few on navigation, weather and tide tables.

Cathy wondered curiously about a man who seemed to have come from nowhere and belonged nowhere but in the grim little rectangular space anchored on the coast. She thought romantically of all the legends she'd read about heroes without a home searching for something, some essence of meaning to their lives, searching for something that soothed their restlessness and gave them peace—was Travis someone in need of peace—the ones who searched for Holy Grails and went on odysseys and crusades and lived lonely lives. Was Travis that kind of man?

Remembering the images she'd awakened with, Cathy got a pen and pad from her purse and sat at the table to begin a poem. The clean white page lay open and challenging until she put the first words down.

All heroes are explorers and solitary men
Who touch the earth only in my dreams
Then sail away again. . . .

She wrote and edited for a long time, so deep in her work that when the door opened again only fifteen minutes later, she was startled. Travis stood with a scowl on his face. There was a grease streak across a brow and down the side of his nose. His hands were grimy, and his hair was wet again. Cathy wondered if he ever got sick considering the almost thoughtless way he took care of himself.

"Lunch is ready," she said in a quiet voice, looking to see if he was still angry.

Travis nodded briefly, closing the door and taking off his raincoat. "I'll wash up—" he began.

"I'll get the food—" she started, their words crossing. She got up from the table, holding her notebook in front of her. Travis turned from the coatrack. They were within a foot of each other, standing awkwardly.

"I see those things fit you all right," he muttered, although he also made quick note of the fact that the denim jeans were molded to her slender legs and curved bottom rather nicely.

Cathy stood staring at him, and then her dark eyes rounded and flashed impatiently. The collar of her plaid shirt stood up at the back of her neck, framing her neck and giving emphasis to her square jaw in a feminine, soft way. "If I had on a potato sack, you'd never notice. I've decided that your bark is worse than your bite and I'm perfectly safe with you. I'm dressed like a boy, and my knee is sticking out!" Then she chuckled softly in self-derision, thinking she was indeed an unattractive sight.

Travis blinked, confused at the incredible speech. Then his brow cleared, and he suddenly started laughing. The sound was rich and deep, and Cathy's attention was caught by it, somehow relieved that he could laugh. Travis thought better of telling her that she hardly looked like a boy or that her naked knees were the last thing on his mind. But then it occurred to him what it was that set her off. He shook his head ruefully, because it only confirmed his impression of her as being very young, but more than that, very inexperienced. Travis swallowed the rest of his amusement.

"I never said you weren't attractive, Cathy." He drawled her name, using it for the first time as he thoughtfully ran the back of his knuckles gently down her cheek.

Cathy stared at him, thinking he was still being indulgent. But his light-colored eyes were serious now, taking in her dark curly hair, the questioning eyes, and letting his gaze drop to her mouth.

"What were you writing? A diary? A journal? Something about me?" he teased.

"I—I was working on a poem . . . about clouds," she improvised.

"What about clouds?" Travis asked as he moved to the sink and ran the water.

Cathy thought and shrugged. "I was thinking how much clouds remind me of other things. Somehow clouds take on different shapes."

Travis shook his head and gave a dry laugh of sarcasm. "What an imagination you have."

"That's why I'm a writer," Cathy informed him evenly, sure now that Travis probably didn't have an ounce of imagination in him. "I just feel there are other beautiful ways to see them."

"They're not always pretty, you know. They also bring storms," Travis said with meaning, reminding her inadvertently of her reaction to the storm of the previous day.

"So you watch clouds, too?" she asked with a smile.

"Sort of. I chase them for the National Weather Service. Take my word for it. There's nothing romantic about them." Travis washed his face and hands as Cathy dished the soup into bowls. "When I'm up in a plane tracking cloud positions, formations and size, I can only wonder how much damage is going to be done when they finally burst over the land. That's hardly pretty and romantic!"

"You probably know nothing about romance, either!" Cathy muttered petulantly under her breath.

Travis wiped his face and hands dry and scowled at her. "Let's eat!" he said roughly.

They were seated in uncomfortable silence at the small table, concentrating on their food. Cathy gave Travis furtive looks, establishing again that he was a handsome man, even if somewhat truculent. They both finally relaxed, and seeing that Travis was enjoying what he ate, Cathy asked if he wanted more soup.

She was leaning over his shoulder, pouring it into his bowl, when Travis suddenly sat back in his chair out of the way, his shoulder coming to rest against Cathy's chest. Travis turned his head to apologize, bringing his head close to her. He was so close that Cathy could see the separate ring of color specks that made up his eye color. It was also close enough for her to notice a scar above his left eye, but under the brow, and another, nearly two inches long, near the temple but partially hidden by his dark thick hair. Abruptly, Travis turned back to the table, leaving her staring at the back of his head.

Cathy was suddenly reminded of leaning into him the night before as the clapping of thunder left her nerves raw with fright. There had been a gentleness to his holding and comforting her, an understanding that belied the hard and rough exterior he presented. Travis was beginning to be a contradiction to Cathy, showing the world one face, perhaps out of necessity, while being something different inside. Blinking away her thoughts, Cathy put the pot away and returned to the table.

She glanced hesitantly at him. "Are you feeling better this morning?" she asked, swirling around in her soup absently with the spoon.

"Why shouldn't I be?" Travis asked, lifting his own spoon to his pursed lips.

"Well, I just thought that after that bad dream you had last night…" She let her voice deliberatey trail off.

The spoon stopped momentarily in midair before Travis slowly finished the movement and thoughtfully sipped the soup. "I don't have dreams at night," he stated evenly.

Cathy was confused. Then she realized that he was being evasive. "I suppose you don't remember me waking you up from one in the middle of the night."

He raised a dark sardonic brow. "I remember waking up to find you rubbing my stomach." The voice drawled low in amusement.

Cathy blushed, gnawing on her lip. She picked up part of her sandwich and nibbled on a corner. "Who's Mitch?" she tried again.

Travis cast her a dangerous, impatient look from his clear eyes. It was like suddenly facing a great cat about to attack. "Let it go, Cathy," he warned her, his eyes narrowing at her.

Cathy hesitated again, sensing that perhaps she was getting more personal than he wanted. "I—I just thought…" She shrugged. "You seemed to be in pain."

There was a pause while Travis's eyes, not actually seeing her at the moment, wandered over her face. "I was too tired to feel anything last night," he stated moodily, ending the discussion. "And what about you? Are you better?" he asked suddenly, offhandedly.

Cathy stared round-eyed at him. "Me? I don't have bad dreams!"

Travis took a bite out of his sandwich and carefully studied her. "Not bad dreams, maybe. But you're scared as hell of storms," he said, watching her closely.

Cathy blanched. Yes, and was it really any different from what he'd gone through even though he wouldn't admit to it or didn't want to talk about it? Now that the tables were turned, she understood his reticence.

"I know. It's very childish, but—"

"I'm not making fun of you. I just wondered why," Travis said quietly.

Cathy looked suspiciously at him and saw only interest.

But she, too, became equally taciturn. "It's...a long, uninteresting story," she responded. Travis looked at her a moment longer before shrugging indifferently and finishing his lunch.

He finally stood up and helped carry the used dishes to the galley. "I have to go work on that furnace," he informed her, "or there'll be no hot water to wash with later and your things will take all night to dry." He moved around her toward his raincoat and a floor chest that, when opened, contained a number of heavy tools.

"Can I help?" Cathy asked at once, not wanting to be alone possibly for hours.

"It's still raining out. You'll get wet," Travis said, putting on the slicker.

"I think I've been wet ever since I arrived in Florida!" Cathy answered in exasperation. Travis frowned at her, considering. "Maybe I can help! I can at least hold your tools."

"Why not," he finally agreed. "You might as well earn your keep." Travis located another slicker. It was much too big for Cathy, like the T-shirt she'd slept in, but it provided excellent cover. There were no extra boots, however, and she had to make do with her already-ruined leather shoes.

The furnace was on an upper deck and usually fed heat into the interior of the houseboat by way of a tank. Silently, Travis went to work on the greasy mechanisms, the open roof of the furnace serving as protection against the rain on the coils and wires. Cathy knelt beside him, passing him the tools as they were needed. There was no conversation, just an occasional command from Travis or a muttered oath as some gear or part stubbornly remained inoperative. After nearly three hours with no discernible headway being made, Cathy deserted her post, much to the impatient grumblings of Travis, who declared her a poor assistant. But Cathy ignored him, going below and returning half an hour later with a more powerful flashlight and a thermos of hot coffee. Travis accepted both with a grunt of bare acknowledgment.

It was almost dark before he let out a deep sigh, closed

down the unit and gathered his tools. "Well, that's all I can do. Let's go see if it works."

Cathy got up stiffly and followed Travis back to the lower deck. Inside could be heard the cracking and knocking of dry pipes as vapors and water circulated through the system. Within an hour they had hot water. Cathy playfully applauded his good work.

Travis gave her a mock bow. "I owe it all to clean living," he quipped sarcastically, nonetheless accepting her praise in good humor. "And since I did most of the work, I get to take the first shower!"

"That sounds fair," Cathy said, laughing. "And since you worked so hard, I'll make dinner."

Cathy decided to make use of the other things Travis had purchased and began the workings for spaghetti carbonara. She had just finished frying bacon when Travis entered the galley behind her, headed toward the shower. Cathy happened to glance over her shoulder and saw that he had completely stripped off his clothing and had only a bath towel wound around his narrow hips. Again she was made aware of the lean, firm body, the sculptured smooth chest and his long muscled legs covered with dark hair. Cathy turned back quickly to her skillet before she could be caught staring, a curious tension twisting inside her stomach.

By the time Travis had showered and dressed, Cathy had dinner ready. They sat down once more to eat, but this time in an atmosphere that was oddly charged and electrified. It only seemed to increase as the meal continued. It was as if the coming night had closed in tightly around them and they were again confronted with being alone together in the closeness of the barge. Suddenly, there was a heightened sense each had of the other in a space they would again share for the night.

Travis watched her openly during the meal, giving her more attention and consideration than he had since they'd met. He liked what he saw, and she *was* attractive—just so damned young!

"I suppose you should stay the night," Travis said with studied casualness when he finished eating.

Cathy glanced briefly at him, her cheeks coloring. "I—I suppose I'll have to. My clothes—"

"Yes, I know."

"I—I hope you don't mind. I don't want to be a bother."

Travis quirked a brow, his eyes searching her face. Her dark sable eyes were filled with open appeal. "I think I can survive one more night of being inconvenienced," he drawled caustically.

"I'll sleep on the couch," Cathy offered in a rush to hide her discomfort.

"It doesn't matter. I was perfecly comfortable—"

"No, you weren't. It's much too short for you. You kicked the clothing rack over in the dark, remember?"

Travis gave her a rueful smile. "Afraid your things will get wet again?"

She shrugged. "No, I just think you'll sleep better in your own bed."

A wicked gleam sparkled in his green eyes. "We could share the bed," he suggested, but Cathy knew he was teasing her again, trying to shock her with an image of himself that was indifferent and uncaring. She threw his amusement back at him.

"No, thank you. The way you sleep I'll end up strangled!"

Cathy had only meant to continue the banter between them, but the color drained from Travis's face, and his mouth clamped into a straight line.

"That's true. I could be a killer for all you know." His eyes stared hard at her.

"I don't...believe that," Cathy whispered confidently, not backing down from the decidedly ominous aura about him.

Travis got up and stalked slowly toward her, the lights throwing his face into shadows again. For a moment Cathy did become apprehensive, seeing something from inside him that quickly crept over his strong male features and then was gone. But it wasn't a threat of danger. "You should," he said roughly, a hand suddenly grabbing her chin.

Cathy didn't allow herself to gasp in surprise, although her dark eyes widened as she stared up at him and felt his hand tilt her head back.

"I could hurt you, Cathy."

Cathy swallowed, and her lips parted to speak, but Travis lowered his head suddenly, his mouth instantly covering hers in possession that was total and unexpected. His tongue at once plundered into her mouth to explore boldly, while a free hand settled on her breast to gently squeeze and massage through her borrowed clothing.

Cathy grew still. And although she didn't respond, neither did she make any protest or move to free herself. She just let Travis have his way, and when he finally released her, her expression was only one of bewildered questioning. The sudden silence between them allowed now for other revelations, as well. Travis saw trust in Cathy as she stared round-eyed and curious at him. Cathy saw a combination of confusion and wonder in his face.

"I don't believe you'd hurt me," she whispered. "I—I don't believe you would hurt anyone."

For a moment longer Travis stared at her. "There are many kinds of hurt, Cathy," he said almost bleakly, almost talking to himself. Then he blinked to focus on her upturned face again, looking at her full mouth and its now-moist, parted surface. "Let's hope you never have to find out about them."

Then he bent to kiss her again, the roughness gone, to be replaced by a light touch that was exploratory and curious. The kiss he took this time was gentle and so much a surprise that Cathy felt herself responding. But just as abruptly as he'd grabbed her, Travis let her go.

"I'll do the cleaning up while you take a shower," he said stiffly, his eyes glaring at her.

Cathy swallowed and nodded, going off slowly, automatically, to get her towel and T-shirt. By the time she'd showered and washed the rainwater out of her hair, the galley had been cleared and everything put away. Dressed in the red T-shirt and with the towel wrapped around her hair as on the night before, she found Travis spreading out linens on the couch. He turned from his chore to find her standing close by, her arms filled with clothing held like a shield in front of her body. They stared at each other silently.

It seemed pointless for Cathy to say she had to leave in the morning. And it was awkward to say, "Thank you for letting me spend two days with you." So nothing was said about the matter, although from the silence and speculative glances much was being thought by both of them. Cathy dropped her eyes first and sat down in a chair half turned away from him as she began to towel-dry her hair. She didn't hear Travis come up behind her and stiffened when she felt his hands cover her own and gently remove them. Then Travis himself began to use his own hands to work the towel back and forth over her hair. Soon Cathy relaxed and began to enjoy his ministrations. She closed her eyes and felt the gentle, though awkward, massaging of Travis's hands.

Cathy had no idea how long it went on. But suddenly the movements stopped. She opened her eyes and turned to look up questioningly at Travis. He slowly slid the towel from her hair to drape it around her neck and over her shoulders. There was an intense look in his green eyes that was also half caressing. The muscles were tensing in his jaw, and his beard-covered face somehow looked dangerously compelling.

Travis grabbed hold of the towel ends and began to pull, forcing Cathy to her feet to face him. She stared at him, mesmerized by the lazy, sensual consideration he gave her. It was a seductive questioning that alerted Cathy suddenly to the real significance of being alone with this man. But she wasn't afraid of him—just totally aware of his power and virility.

Travis tugged on the towel ends, and Cathy came a step closer until she could smell the soap and shampoo on him from his own shower. She could see his eyes dilating from the changes in light and emotion. And she could see his nostrils flare as he in turn could smell her, shower-fresh and pretty, terribly young and warm. She blinked as Travis began to lower his head toward her.

In twenty-four hours of being in two small rooms together he'd made no overt passes toward her. But in just twenty-four hours she'd come to feel safe and comfortable with him, and she wasn't going to struggle if he was going to hold and kiss her. She wanted him to, to prove that he was wrong and had only been teasing her with his threats of hurting her. She wanted him to show he was attracted to her.

Nonetheless, it was a shock to feel his mouth again, firm and wide on her own softer lips. His face hair was wonderfully soft and almost furry, brushing on her chin and cheeks. Travis at first just applied a light touch, very different from the one earlier. Then he pulled back just enough to ply a second kiss from her. Cathy's lips parted on their own. Travis kissed her yet again, seeming to tease more than to really be kissing her with any passion.

Then he moved back completely from her, his lowered eyes locked to the moist curves of her mouth. Slowly, he brought his eyes up to hers. "You're much too trusting. You know that? he said hoarsely. "You should know better."

Cathy smiled ruefully. "I suppose. Chad always used to say it would get me in trouble one of these days."

There was a pause. "Who's Chad?" Travis asked tightly in a low tone, his eyes narrowing.

"My brother," Cathy responded readily.

Travis visibly relaxed. A hand slowly raised, and a finger traced the soft line of her jaw, ending at her chin. "He's right, you know," he answered. He dropped his hand abruptly. "Good night, Cathy," Travis said suddenly. It was firm. And final.

Cathy stared at him in confusion and was still staring after him as he released her and walked away into the galley. He opened a cabinet, took out a gin bottle, got a glass and disappeared into the back room and his own bed. The light went out, and Cathy was left staring into the dark.

CATHY FOUND that she could not sleep well. She tossed and turned fitfully on the narrow couch, not because she was uncomfortable but because she half expected to hear a repeat of the night before, with Travis caught in some nightmare that terrorized his soul, no matter what he might deny during the day. But the strain of listening had Cathy wound up like a coiled spring, and exhaustion sent her into a shallow sleep where the slightest sound registered and caused her to jump. Oddly enough, when Travis did indeed begin to have his dream again, it was several minutes before his moaning anguish got through to Cathy. At once she was up and, although a little groggy from her own sleep, made her way to the back room and Travis.

Cathy didn't hesitate at all this time in sitting on the edge of the bed. But unlike the night before, Travis wasn't twisting about. Tonight his body was tautly straight, the sheets tangled around his waist and thighs. His arms were stretched back over his head, and his hands tightly gripped the edge of the headboard. His face, arms and chest were bathed in sweat.

"Travis…" Cathy began softly.

"I'm trying…" Travis gritted between clenched teeth. "Mitch! I—I'm trying!"

"Travis, shh…it's all right. Wake up."

Cathy wiped his forehead. He moaned, turning his head away. Cathy touched his chest, and the skin was wet and hot. She received a kind of shock. It completely stilled her for a moment in surprise. It was…something from Travis. Cathy felt it through her fingertips, and it rippled quickly through her body. Cathy's heart contracted, and her concern deepened. Everything that Travis was experiencing became important to her—personal. It was as if she could feel his pain, could absorb it through the bare points where his body touched hers. It was as if she knew all about him, or at least the raw feelings and emotions that coursed through him. She had become sensitive to him, making him unique to her.

"Oh, Travis," Cathy whispered shakily with feeling. "What is it that hurts you so?"

Cathy's foot brushed against something on the floor that then rolled away. It was the empty liquor bottle. Next to it, her crumpled red bandanna. Cathy picked it up and began wiping away the heated moisture from Travis's body, murmuring to him all the while. It was like having to soothe a distraught child, only Cathy's complete awareness of his sinewy naked body declared that he was no child. And his persona, right down to his current agitation, was distinctly adult.

Very slowly Travis began to relax his body, though his breathing remained hurried and he still clutched the headboard. Then, suddenly, as if someone had yelled his name, his eyes flew open. Startled and eerie in the dark, he stared fixedly at Cathy for a long tight moment.

"You're awake now. It's just another dream." Cathy's hand stroked his jaw. The rest of his body went limp at the soothing tone of her voice. Slowly, Travis brought his hands down.

He put them on Cathy's arms and slowly rode the cool, slender length of her limbs to her shoulders. The movement made her shiver, because it felt so personal and caressing. And at first she thought he was just reassuring himself that she was real and he was indeed awake. But then Travis began to close his arms around her, bringing her slowly down and against his hard damp body.

"Cathy..." Travis murmured in a broken, hoarse voice.

At once Cathy resisted, bracing her arms on his chest and not allowing the elbows to bend completely. But she was no match for Travis's male strength, and he was determined.

"Travis, no..." Cathy said, but her voice lacked firmness. In any case, he seemed not to have heard or chose to ignore her.

Cathy's elbows gave in, and with a surprised gasp she found herself lying against Travis's chest. One strong arm anchored around her waist, the other over her shoulder, his fingers buried in her curly hair. His skin smelled sweaty and male. His breath smelled faintly of alcohol. Cathy tried again to pull away from him, much too aware of him physically.

"Keep still! I won't hurt you. I promise," Travis whispered roughly, immediately stilling her actions with

the unexpected, clear command of his voice. "I just—
Just let me hold you for a while."

His request threw Cathy off guard, although he was
hardly asking for permission. But Cathy let her body relax
against him. And sure now that she wouldn't object further, Travis let out a lightly held breath and gentled his
hold around her.

Cathy lay still, feeling as if some lifeline was passing back
and forth between them. He held her as if he garnered some
sort of strength from her. Perhaps only calm and peace.
But then Travis began to roll his body to the side, bringing
the lighter weight of Cathy's body with him. Travis swung
her clear over his own and onto the bed next to him.

"Stay..." Cathy thought he murmured, and something
else she couldn't make out, because his voice, muffled
against her hair, had gone tired and drowsy. He settled her
comfortably in his arms for his own purposes, not waiting
for any further responses from Cathy but taking her silence and malleability as acquiescence.

For a long time they lay that way, until the weight of
Travis's arms and his heavy, exhausted breathing told
Cathy he was asleep. For an even longer time she listened
to the sound of it and tentatively touched his body as
he slept. Her fingers moved curiously over his chest,
smoothing in fascination over the hard planes of muscle.
His heartbeat was very strong and rhythmic. Cathy could
imagine a poetic cadence to it, as if there were words repeating over and over a message to her. She let her hand
lay familiarly over his heart and snuggled into his shoulder. His reflexes were quick to tighten his hands on her
and then relax when she stopped moving. And although
Cathy thought she couldn't possibly do that, she, too,
went to sleep.

It was sometime much later in her half sleep that a languid warmth assailed Cathy's limbs. Her body moved instinctively to press closer to the source, responding to
hands upon her skin. She thought of Brian, except that
Brian had never stroked her that way. Still, a hand, large
and purposeful, was sliding across her stomach up over
her rib cage to a breast.

Cathy momentarily lost her thoughts and comparisons and, sighing, arched her back in sleepy delight as her nipple was stimulated briefly into a hard little peak. She moved her hips and encountered the pressure of bold, taut flesh. Identifying it brought her awake and out of her dream state, into the melting throes of desire. It was Travis who held her, not Brian. The muscles in her stomach and loins curled and tightened in a sensuous arch that made her feel limp all over. Yet the delicious feelings were suddenly pulled in check when Cathy realized that Travis was now attempting to remove her T-shirt.

She tried to cross her arms to hold the shirt in place, but Travis quickly shifted his hands to her bare hip and bottom. Cathy gasped and reached to grab his wrists.

"Travis!"

His hands came back to the T-shirt, pulling it up and over her head in a quick gesture. Cathy tried to bend a knee into his stomach to keep them apart.

"Cathy, stop fighting me," Travis ground out hoarsely into her ear. The T-shirt was tossed to the floor.

"Travis, you...you said you wouldn't...hurt me," Cathy said breathlessly. The mind wanted to stop him, remind him that they were strangers, but her traitorous body tingled all over from his touch and seemed more inclined to let him continue. With admirable resolve, however, Cathy braced her hands against his chest in a last-ditch effort to keep control. Travis rolled her onto her back.

He grabbed both wrists and pinned her hands next to her head as he lay half on top of her. Cathy gasped again and stopped moving. He was completely aroused and urgent against her. Her heart skipped a beat, and Cathy swallowed hard, fighting against giving in. Travis's breathing was also shallow, his breath hot in her ears. Cathy's eyes drifted close.

"I'm not hurting you, am I?" he drawled. He turned his head, trying to reach her mouth with his. Cathy turned away.

"Re-remember what you said. I—I'm not your type!" she reminded him for a second time, her voice breathy.

"Did I say that?" he mumbled, his tongue flicking at the corner of her mouth. He kissed her chin, his beard a tingling sensation. Then he lifted his head to look at her. Out of curiosity to see what stopped him for a moment, Cathy turned her head to gaze at him, too. She was held fascinated by the sudden light in his eyes. "I must have been drunk," Travis said seductively, and bent to kiss her.

After a moment Cathy melted toward the feeling he generated and some innate emotion surrounding them both. Her apprehension was lessened rather than increased. With a soft, helpless sound she went limp. She began to enjoy the kiss, and also to some extent examine and compare it. For no reason that made any sense, she suddenly remembered the first time she'd been kissed.

She'd been fourteen and at one of the few parties she'd been allowed to go to without Chad as chaperon. The party had been presumed safe and innocuous enough, as it was only down the block from her home. But it had been attended by adolescent boys and girls hovering between childhood and young adulthood, and curiosity was rampant. There had been much less innocent groping than usual, and everyone seemed intent on proving they weren't novices in the mysteries of hot hugs and kisses. The lights had gone out. There had been moist wet sounds, a few giggles, a few "ouches" and "be careful." Cathy had been suddenly wrestled against the sofa cushions, and a pair of soft, inexperienced lips pressed wetly to her own, cutting off her breathing. She'd lain limp then, unresisting, not angry so much as surprised. Cathy had been decidedly underwhelmed by the encounter, wondering what the excitement was all about.

By eighteen she knew little more about herself and her own body responses but had finally met one or two boys her age with some practice, if not finesse, to understand better the phenomena. And, of course, with the rest of normal young development and curiosity she'd discovered that kissing and being held felt good. But there her experience, pleasure and knowledge ended. But now Cathy realized she was with a man who knew exactly what he was doing, and what he wanted from her. Her curiosity was once more aroused.

Travis now found her mouth soft and answering. His tongue encouraged her to respond, and with a sigh she parted her lips to give him entry. The joy of being kissed with knowledgeable care and expertise vanquished the last of her resistance, and her own dawning need eliminated her doubts, as well.

It also came to Cathy, perhaps perversely under the circumstances, that Brian had never made her feel quite this way and that his kisses had been rather pedestrian. He always seemed not to want to really make love to her so much as to pet and stroke her. And while it now seemed true that Travis was not particularly intent on her reaction to him, he nonetheless was more capable of obtaining a willing response. A kind of heady euphoria seemed to be gathering within Cathy, frightening and certainly new, and she could barely catch her breath from one sensation to the next.

Travis suddenly released her wrists, and automatically they wound themselves around his neck. With his mouth locked to hers, drawing the very breath from her, Travis concentrated on thoroughly searching out the rest of her trembling body. A hand covered her breast, the fingers again massaging the nipple, making it turgid. The hand moved down her torso to her stomach, around her hip, to curve fully under her bottom and draw her tightly against him.

Travis separated her knees and shifted his weight. He dragged his mouth to her jaw, her neck and throat.

"Travis..." Cathy moaned his name weakly, knowing now what was to happen and suddenly frantic that she should say something to him. But he reclaimed her mouth and moved to bring them together. His thrust was direct and sudden. They both stiffened with shock then and lay still for a long shuddering moment. Travis murmured to her, but it was too late to go back and impossible not to go on.

Cathy moved inexpertly but suggestively and with excruciatingly slow cadence they became synchronized. She was suddenly aware of every nuance of him. She could feel Travis, sense him all around her and through her. She felt suspended and unreal as their heartbeats and sighs and touching were offered and matched one to the other. She was lifted out of the world and was Venus, Isolde, Juliet, because this was still part of a dream and not connected at all to what she really was or had been.

Travis caressed her until she was shaking and silent tears of surprise squeezed from her closed eyes. She found herself clinging to him as if she were on the edge of something and might fall. But she didn't. Moving deeply but slowly, Travis purged himself of some emotion, rid himself of some demon. Finally, he sighed deeply, holding her sweetly at last in his own ultimate satisfaction with her.

For a while there were only thundering heartbeats and rich deep breaths of air. Their eyes drifted open to confront each other in wonder. Travis's eyes widened upon noticing the tears in hers. He misunderstood them, however, and his jaw tightened in self-derisive anger, darkening his brows and flaring his nostrils. With a shaky finger he reached to brush the tears away. "Don't..." he croaked out emotionally.

Overwhelmed and surprised by the depth of what had happened between them, Travis had an instinctive need to kiss her tenderly. He felt that he had not simply joined with her to make love and then separate at the end. They had joined bodies, touched souls, journeyed through space and time, destroyed part of the past, given rise to a new beginning....

And in some as yet inexplicable manner, they had saved each other's lives.

Chapter Five

Cathy sat resting her hands against her stomach with her eyes closed, remembering the strength, closeness and feel of Travis against her. Remembering the delicious sense of belonging that she'd known that night back in April. She realized, too, that her having slept with Travis created a physical affinity between them even as it also broke the emotional ties with Brian. But the affinity with Travis was only supposed to last the one night.

Instead, she'd returned to Baltimore and thought about him almost constantly, trying to convince herself that theirs had just been a chance encounter and was unimportant. It didn't matter that at the time she'd fought the desire to stay and learn more about this man who now possessed her. But now everything was different. Despite what her good sense, her fears, her fantasies, her heart, told her, she was forever tied to Travis no matter what decision she now made about the baby.

Even on that last sultry night in Key West, Cathy had wondered at having found Travis, someone she seemed destined to be a part of, only to realize quickly that in the morning she really would have to leave.

It had been just at the point that night ended but dawn hadn't begun that Cathy became aware of Travis's hands gently gliding over her body again. She murmured something incoherent and sleepy as he reached for her, kissing her mouth awake when she was slow in answering. He pulled her beneath him, weaving his fingers into her soft dark hair and staring intently into her rich sable eyes.

"It would be so easy to love you," Travis whispered, his

eyes thoroughly searching over her face, watching the dreamy sparkle in them. His hips pressed urgently against her, and he started to love her again. This time, free of the bad dreams, he led her to complete ecstasy, too.

The morning sunlight through the round porthole of the houseboat made a distorted circle on the wooden floor. Cathy stepped out of the bed and cautiously into the light, leaving Travis still deeply asleep and undisturbed. He never moved as silently she dressed and retrieved her belongings. She stood for a very long moment of indecision, looking down on this man who'd come to represent all that the words "independent," "adventure," "romance," implied. She wished there was something to leave him, not knowing yet that she had indeed left him with a priceless gift.

Travis lay sprawled over the space of the bed, his naked athletic body bronzed and sculptured. Cathy pulled the thin blanket up and over his legs and waist. She wondered when was the last time he'd slept as soundly as he did right now, as she was leaving him, unable—unwilling—to say good-bye. She wondered how often he had bad dreams, how often he was alone with them. Cathy thought briefly of staying a bit longer just in case he woke in terror again. Another hesitancy grabbed at her as she wondered if he would again reach for her.

Yet in the end Cathy fled, because she knew with a certainty early in that new day that if she didn't leave while sanity and daylight prevailed, she never would.

Cathy knew now that she'd have to tell Travis that she was pregnant. She'd have to let him know that their one night of comforting and loving each other had sowed seed that was growing within her. But Cathy didn't really know why she had to tell him. Suppose he didn't remember her or didn't care? Suppose he wasn't even there? What if he'd left Key West forever and gone off to another part of the world?

"Will there be anything else, miss?" the waitress asked Cathy patiently, drawing her back from the near panic that was beginning belatedly to possess her.

"N-no. No, thank you. I—I'm finished."

The waitress nodded and left the check under the edge of the empty teacup. On the window to her left, Cathy's attention was caught by a trailing raindrop zigzagging down the windowpane. It called to mind Travis's comment to her that clouds were not always pretty, that they also brought gray skies and rain. She sat for a long time, considering this watery release from the heavens, like her release from within, the water falling exactly like so many tears of sorrow.

CATHY GOT UP restlessly from her chair and wandered over to the window. There was no rain that day. As a matter of fact, it was the kind of clear-sky day Florida was supposed to be famous for. No feathery formations now, but smooth baby blue stretching on and on. She could almost see clear to the coast. She wondered what Travis was doing. She wondered if he ever thought about her or if he had forgotten all about her and gone back to his usual existence, whatever that was.

Cathy suspected that it was lonely and unhappy. She remembered his beautiful but sad eyes, a window to a past obviously filled with torment and pain if his dreams were anything to go by. And she remembered his sensually full but somewhat cruel mouth, rarely smiling, uttering cynicism and sarcastic humor. With a sudden tension in her stomach she wondered what his reaction would be to finding out she was pregnant. But she didn't know enough about him to even guess. As it was, Cathy didn't know yet what it meant to her, to have a child and be a mother.

The door to the office opened, and Elizabeth Harris came back in, closing it behind her.

"Well, everything seems okay. I wouldn't worry about that spotting yet or the occasional cramps. But I would like to do a sonogram and get some pictures of the cervix. That could be a problem." Elizabeth sat down at her desk as she talked, adjusting her glasses and smiling at Cathy.

Cathy gnawed at her bottom lip. "Elizabeth..."

The woman lifted her head and regarded Cathy. She'd been relieved when Cathy had called her several days ago. She recognized that Cathy had come to that phase of her reactions when she didn't want to be alone and needed to talk. And so, under the guise of medical tests and questions, Cathy made an appointment to come in. But since arriving, Cathy had not attempted to broach the subject of the baby and what she wanted to do. Elizbeth waited, giving her the time she needed to find a footing in the problem.

"Elizabeth, I—I've decided I have to tell the—the baby's father." The word came out in a kind of surprised whisper, because she immediately associated the word "father" with her own, someone loving and kind and supportive. To pair it with Travis seemed alien. At least as strange as pairing "mother" with herself.

"If you really want to," Elizabeth commented evenly.

"I feel I have to," Cathy amended. "I—I think he has a right to at least know that."

Elizabeth tilted her head and pursed her lips. "How are you feeling about it?" she asked quietly, watching Cathy.

Cathy blinked several times and massaged her temple absently with a hand.

"Strange," she said vaguely. "And different."

"But you're not any different, Cathy. The things that people loved and admired in you are all still there."

"But that's for other people. What about me? I—I feel so—so out of control! I don't think I can handle this. I have nothing to go on, no guidelines, no rules, no experience!"

"Most people don't. No one has ever given birth, raised a child, learned all the pitfalls and the unexpected and then gone back to do it over again."

Cathy walked over to the desk and looked helplessly at the older woman. "I don't know enough about life to teach a child anything. I don't know enough about myself!"

Elizabeth could feel Cathy's confusion and anguish, but she could in no way tell her what she should do. "Are you saying you may not want to go through with the pregnancy?"

Cathy blinked again and hesitated. She still hadn't actually thought in terms of an abortion. "What I'm saying is

I—I'm scared. And I need some time to think about this."

"I understand that. Just remember that more than anything else, being a mother means love. Lots of it. And the things you teach a child are things you learn about yourself, too. You can grow and learn together."

Cathy worried at her lip and clenched her hands, her dark eyes rounded in apprehension. Yes, she was afraid. But there was also the part of her that wanted this child, and that was harder to explain and understand. It felt instinctive to want it, because it was hers. But also because it was part of Travis.

But first she had to tell him and to find out if he was as real as she remembered him. Or had he been that dream she wrote about? A figment of her imagination who had sailed... or faded away?

THE BRIGHT JUNE SUNSHINE did much for the city of Key West, if one didn't look and examine too closely. The sun bounced streaks of light off the slapdash atmosphere, making the place charming and offbeat, busy and alive. It was shown at its best. Cathy had missed all of it, even the second time she'd been there.

It was just after she'd moved to Florida officially, and thoughts of Travis and her time with him filled her mind. She wondered if he was still in Key West, and pure curiosity and a secret enticement led her there again, this time with full knowledge of what she sought. Many times she wondered what would have ultimately happened had she stayed with him that morning back in April. Cathy had been too unsure at the time to do so. And during her second time in Key West the uncertainty had been replaced by romantic interest and a desire to see him again. This time it was necessity.

Cathy's second trip to Key West, however, had ended with her not seeing Travis. She had no trouble making her way back to that sad street where the tavern she'd taken refuge in was nestled. It stood ancient-looking and unique between two warehouses. It was simply called the Waterfront Café, although it was some distance from the wharf.

Cathy had arrived wearing a yellow sundress, making her a pretty incongruity in the grim surroundings. She stood staring at the café entrance as if it were a mirage and jumped when the door opened unexpectedly and two sailors, obviously having drunk their way through lunch, emerged, stumbling off down an alleyway. Cathy straightened her spine and, taking a deep breath, moved with determination toward the café entrance.

She pushed through into the dim interior and had an immediate sense of déjà vu. Her head automatically swung to the table off to the side where she'd first seen Travis in his wet yellow slicker, half expecting to see him again. Against her whole urge to see him again, however, Cathy breathed a sigh of relief to see that the table was empty.

There were a few men and one well-rounded woman with hair an absurd shade of red sitting at a number of places along the bar. Cathy was surprised to see the one woman until she looked more carefully and saw clearly the ravages of age, a hard life and drink etched on the woman's bloated features. Then sadly it became clear that this woman did belong there, too.

Cathy walked over to the bar and waited until the bartender, Joe, made his way to her end. His eyes looked at her blankly, apparently not recognizing her from weeks ago. Cathy wasn't sure if she should smile, say hello or what. And if she couldn't even begin with that much, she felt she'd never be able to bring up the question of how to find Travis. But Joe proved her wrong and settled her first question at once. He stopped in front of her, looking her up and down as he wiped his hands on a less than clean dish rag.

"So...you're back. Are you lost again?" he asked evenly. It was hard to tell if he really cared one way or another. His chosen way of life had shown this ageless, brawny man all there was to know. It held no more surprises for him whatsoever. He was neither happy nor unhappy, nor did he care if other people were or were not. Joe knew a multitude of people—all kinds from all walks of life. He called none of them friends or even acquaintances. But he never forgot anyone who passed through his doors.

Cathy was somewhat relieved that he recognized her, after all. It was like an anchor that made that rainy night in April real. She smiled tentatively, not sure how to respond to him and his indifferent air.

"Yes, I'm back. So I guess I didn't get lost."

Joe didn't respond, though he kept looking at her as if reading all about Cathy in her shy smile and overlarge dark eyes. He suddenly chuckled soundlessly.

"Hudson's asked about you once or twice. You made quite an impression that night."

Cathy stiffened and furtively looked over her shoulder and around the room to make sure he wasn't there.

"But I'm willing to bet it's Travis you're looking for."

Cathy turned back to him hesitantly. "W-what makes you think that?"

Joe shrugged. Behind the counter he took the time to pop open a can and empty its contents into a glass half filled with ice. He passed the glass to Cathy before answering. "Lots of women come back here looking for him," Joe informed her boldly, unconcerned with how she'd react to the news. He also never concerned himself with other people's feelings. Joe took the position that anyone coming in there was likely able to take care of themselves. And if they weren't, that was still their problem.

Completely nonplussed by his comment, Cathy lifted the drink and took a small nervous sip, the condensation on the glass cooling her suddenly hot hands. Joe watched her calmly, bracing his beefy hands on the counter. Cathy couldn't help finding the words startling, even though she knew they shouldn't have been. Travis was a man women would be drawn to.

"I've never known it to take this long for one of Hoyt's women to show up again. Almost all of 'em do one time or another."

Cathy's stomach flipped over as she wondered dismally how many there were. But almost gratefully she'd learned something else about Travis. One was that he obviously stayed pretty much in the area. And second, she now had his full name—Travis Hoyt. The sound of it was solid and strong, like the man himself. Cathy blinked out of her reverie and looked at Joe. He was still watching her with his disconcerting openness. She hastily finished the soda and pushed the glass away, thanking Joe.

"Have you seen him?" Cathy asked now, a little sorry that she'd come.

"Not for two or three days. But I don't think he's off on reconnaissance. Try down at the marina." Joe now leaned forward and rested his elbows on the counter in front of her. "Do you remember how to get there?" he inquired softly.

Cathy turned pink, because the implication of the question was so blatant and there was no way she could not understand his meaning. She shook her head no.

"Out the door here and to your right for five blocks. Then right again for two more."

Cathy silently nodded and prepared to leave. She wasn't going to feel embarrassed about having returned. Joe could think what he wanted. There was nothing she could do about that. "Thank you for the drink—and your time. You've been very kind."

"I doubt it," Joe said dryly, standing straight again and moving away to a waiting customer. "But good luck to you!"

Cathy followed the directions given her and, when she reached the waterfront, walked slowly along the piers. It seemed to be jam-packed with every kind of pleasure cruiser imaginable. She wondered why anyone who might own such gorgeous and expensive equipment would not be out on the sound on such a day. Other than her one experience on Travis's houseboat, Cathy had never been on a boat, but she now could picture the sheer joy of freedom under a perfect blue sky and over blue-green undulating water. For a long moment, as her eyes glanced over the line of boats, she could see herself lying on an open deck, the sea breeze blowing through her hair, the sun turning her normally warm peach skin tones to a creamy brown. Cathy grimaced playfully. Nice little daydream, but with her luck she'd probably be seasick and turn pea-green!

Cathy had no trouble spotting the double-decker house-boat that was Travis's. She knew it at once, although it didn't look the way her memory had recorded it. For some reason Cathy remembered the hull as being green. It was actually a beautiful shade of ultramarine blue. She thought the houseboat was small and cramped. It was at least thirty-four feet in length. And she thought it would be old, rusting and in disrepair. It was not a new craft, but it was well cared for, not even a small chip visible on its painted surface.

Cathy's heart lurched in her chest, and her cheeks grew once again rosy with a sudden flash vision of Travis strok-ing her naked body on his bed. It was unnerving, and it shocked her, because even the memory was pleasurable. She walked down the length of the pier that would put her closer to the boat. She noticed at once that all the port-holes were open and a previously undetected hatch was lifted allowing sunlight into the boat. There was no sign of anyone, although everything was open. Cathy stood star-ing, almost hypnotized by the scene and all at once terri-fied of seeing Travis again. For an indecisive moment she gnawed at her bottom lip. Then, letting out a small sound of impatience, Cathy turned and quickly rushed away.

She had felt so foolish. Travis wouldn't remember her. Why should he? And worse yet, what if someone else was with him now? But she didn't stay to find out. She left Key West as if pursued by ghosts.

All of it came to mind now as Cathy again found herself walking slowly along the marina until she again found the blue-hulled barge. Again she stood in indecision. And again, feeling the panic, she changed her mind. But there was a sound, a scraping of a chair on the wooden deck, that stopped her; she looked back at the boat. Now she noticed other things. A shirt hanging over a line, lifting lightly in the breeze. She blinked when she spotted a bicy-cle leaning against the side. It was a bright red two-wheeler, meant for a child.

Cathy stared at it and felt the ground go soft under her feet, feeling her head empty of thoughts and her ears buzz. All the hopes that she hadn't yet clarified in her head died. There was more sound, and before Cathy could move away, a woman stepped from the entrance on the main deck with a pail in hand, the contents of which she poured over the side. Curiosity held Cathy still as she watched the woman. She was, perhaps, in her mid-thirties, a little taller than Cathy herself and larger of frame. The woman's shoulder-length hair was blond and straight. She wore a pair of jeans, the legs rolled up almost to her knees, and a strapless white tube top that molded itself to her full curved breasts. She was sort of earthy-looking—and very attractive. And she moved around the craft with a sure familiarity that said she belonged there.

Unaccountably, tears began to blur Cathy's vision. She felt sick inside and so desolate. A question had been answered for her but led to a multitude of others not yet asked. She turned and began to stumble away, hoping she wasn't going to be sick.

"Can I help you?" came a feminine voice that was surprisingly husky in tone.

Cathy jumped and turned around guiltily at the sound. The woman was standing near the planking, squinting against the sun at Cathy, her hands braced on her hips.

"Were you looking for someone?" she asked now.

Cathy felt a hysterical giggle tickle along her throat. Yes, but the person she was looking for, hoping to find, obviously didn't exist. It had all been a fantasy, and she had been dreaming. Travis was no hero, after all. With one hand Cathy gestured helplessly, shaking her head and lifting her shoulders.

"I—I..." was all she managed to get out, annoyed that she was making nothing more than imbecilic mumblings.

Nonetheless, the woman tilted her blond head, trying to catch the meaningless sounds. Then she moved toward the plank barefoot, walking toward Cathy. Cathy could only think that if this was the kind of woman Travis really liked, at least he had good taste. The woman was actually smiling at her as she approached.

"It's so easy to get lost along here. There's a mile-run worth of boats out here." She pointed carelessly over a shoulder but continued to walk, finally stopping a few feet from Cathy. "And after forty or fifty of them they all begin to look alike! What's the name of the boat you want?"

Cathy was fascinated. The woman was so pleasant and friendly. "I—I don't know," she answered softly.

The woman placed her head on a slight angle and quickly, without being obvious, looked Cathy up and down. She pursed her lips. "Are you looking for Travis?" she asked with bright curiosity.

Cathy swallowed and nodded.

"He's not here right now, but he'll be back soon." The woman looked at a black-banded sports watch on her tan wrist. "Actually, I expected him more than an hour ago. He took the kids fishing and probably let them talk him into just one more hour!" She laughed wryly, her blue eyes crinkling around the corners. Her smile and cheerful disposition easily took ten years off her face.

But now that Cathy had more or less adjusted to the idea of this woman belonging here, the mention of two kids, as well, was quickly absorbed. Cathy was already beyond being further shocked and only grew cold and numb inside.

"Are you...Mrs. Hoyt?" Cathy suddenly asked softly, her voice surprisingly clear.

The woman's smile faded, and she blinked in surprise. "Why, yes! I am!" Then she frowned, looking at Cathy in open speculation. "Do I know you?"

Somehow Cathy found it in herself to smile. For a wild moment she was tempted to say, "No, but we have something in common." Instead, she merely shook her head and offered no further explanation.

The woman shrugged. "Well, you're more than welcome to wait. I'm sure Travis will turn up anytime now." She suddenly grinned mischievously. "They didn't take lunch with them, you see, and I fully expect three starving fishermen to descend upon me soon!"

Cathy was suddenly, perversely, tempted to stay just so she could see Travis's reaction to her while in the presence of his family. But there'd be nothing to gain from that but embarrassment all around, and she instantly discarded the idea. So she only shook her head again, taking a step away. "Thank you, but no."

It also rather stunned Cathy that Mrs. Hoyt was not the least bit curious or concerned as to her presence there or her acquaintance with Travis. Certainly there must be people with very modern and open ideas about marriage and relationships, but at that moment, listening to the cheerful and garrulous Mrs. Hoyt, Cathy realized that she herself was probably not one of them. Her experiences had been too few to have changed many of her romantic notions. But just as quickly Cathy's guilt caught up to her as she remembered that, while presumably being promised to Brian, she was now pregnant by another man. Warm blood rushed to her face, making her both hot and dizzy. She took more hurried steps away from the barge and the blonde.

The woman put out her hand as if to stay Cathy. "Well...but...who shall I say was here? Don't you want to leave a message?"

Cathy kept moving, still smiling stiffly, still shaking her head. The message had been private. Her eyes were blurring again. "He rescued me in a storm...a few months ago. I—I only stopped by to—to say thanks."

"Rescued you? Yep! That sounds like my Travis!"

Her Travis. Cathy's stomach sank further.

"Wait! What's your name?"

Cathy hesitated and then shrugged. What difference would it make? *He'll never admit to knowing me.* "Cathy Donnelly...." Cathy watched, puzzled, as the woman slowly stopped smiling. She blinked and squinted again at Cathy, as if to see her more clearly.

"Cathy?" she repeated curiously. But Cathy only waved briefly and turned to walk away completely.

Somehow she made it back to her car and got out of Key West, driving automatically; later, she had no memory of the trip. All the way back tears rolled unchecked down her cheeks, drops of salty water spotting her blouse and slacks. Her quiet sobs went unheard and unsoothed in the car. Cathy hurried to get back. She was desperate to reach Elizabeth Harris at the women's center. But Elizabeth was away at a three-day convention in Atlanta.

"OKAY, YOU TWO. I want you back here in two hours! No ifs, ands or buts about it. Do I make myself clear?"

The voice had the right amount of parental threat in it, but judging from the two quickly fading responses, hastily shouting, "Okay, Mom!" it was doubtful it was taken seriously.

The blond head shook ruefully for a moment, let out an exasperated sigh of defeat at her inability to command instant obedience and turned to the man crouched low over a plastic square basin.

Travis had a half-smoked cigarette dangling out of his mouth, and his eyes and forehead were furrowed in concentration as he scaled and gutted the six freshly caught pompano on the deck beside him. His thick dark hair was in disarray from the wind blowing it forward over his brow, and it fell over a bright folded red bandanna tied rakishly to keep sweat from his eyes. His bare smooth-muscled back was bronzing deeper under the sun, his shoulder and arm muscles pulling and stretching with his present chore. The blonde began to clear the remains of a late lunch from the make-shift table set up on the first deck bow of the craft.

"I thought they'd *never* leave!" she said dramatically.

Travis cast her a brief look with a raised brow. "I had them out all morning. Wasn't that enough time to yourself, or are you having a series of very quick affairs?"

She snapped a dish towel at his back playfully, eliciting an indifferent "Ouch" from him.

"Don't be cute! Who's got time for an affair? Trying to keep up with a ten- and fourteen-year-old is enough to squelch even the thought!" She disappeared momentarily inside the houseboat, and plates were heard settling on the wooden galley counter, silverware clanging in the aluminum sink.

"I keep telling you, Melinda, no one is stopping you

from dating again but yourself. You're attractive and fun to be with, and you have a lot to offer."

Melinda came to the door and leaned on the frame, watching Travis with a wry expression. "Yeah, including two active adolescent boys! Most men aren't looking for ready-made families, Travis. They don't want a package deal."

Travis stopped for a moment to sit back on his heels and contemplate the woman in front of him. He thoughtfully drew on the almost-dead cigarette, instantly rekindling the spark on the end. After a deep drag he took it out of his mouth and exhaled the smoke. "Only Mitch died, Mel. There's no reason for you to bury yourself, too," he said softly, evenly, to her. They stared at each other for long minutes with very similar thoughts and memories.

"You should talk," she responded just as softly, with real empathy laced in the words. She watched a cloud descend over her brother-in-law's face. Travis bent once more over the fish.

There was a long silence until he said, "There are lots of men who are mature enough to deal with a widow with kids."

Melinda grimaced. "Obviousy not enough, judging by my dating record recently."

"I keep telling you to send the boys to Dad for a month or so, so you can go do what you want to for a while. You rate a vacation."

She shrugged diffidently. "Maybe...in any case, getting the boys out of here for two hours is hardly a vacation and not the reason I wanted them gone." She came to the table again and picked up an empty salad bowl, piling four plastic tumblers into it. "Someone came looking for you a while back." Melinda once more slipped inside.

"Oh, yeah? Who?" Travis asked, not much interested. "What did they want?"

Melinda brought a sponge to wipe off the table. "It was something about being rescued. She said her name was Cathy—Cathy Donnelly."

The scaling of the fish went on for another second and then stopped. Travis remained absolutely motionless, and

Melinda turned in curiosity to stare at him. His reaction now was the same as hers had been earlier in the day, and he also repeated the name in a broken voice, in disbelief. Travis stood up to his full six-foot height, and Melinda tilted her head to look up into his face.

"Cathy..." he said again, vaguely. Melinda frowned.

"I take it you don't know or remember another Cathy?"

He didn't respond directly. His eyes flashed bits and pieces of other information.

Melinda shuddered. "God! For a moment when she said Cathy, all I could think of was—"

"Yeah, I know," Travis put in roughly, not letting Melinda finish. "What—what did she look like?" he asked instead.

Melinda hesitated, biting her lip shamefacedly.

Travis sighed impatiently. "Go on... tell me you didn't have your glasses on."

"Okay." She grinned sheepishly. "I didn't have my glasses on."

"Dammit, Melinda! Your vanity—"

"But I did see her—sort of," she hastened to add. "She was...she was about my height," she said referring to her own five-foot six-inch frame, "but a lot thinner! And I think she had curly hair—lots of it! From what I could see, I'd say she was cute!"

Travis listened to his sister-in-law, his body held stiffly and alert, a wariness raising the hairs on the back of his neck. "And that was all she said—that I'd rescued her?" he asked, obviously puzzled.

"That's all. By the way, what did you rescue her from?"

Travis stared trancelike into space, remembering. "A storm. And a dragon," he added mysteriously.

Melinda blinked at him and raised her brows. "Okay, I won't ask!" she said in amusement. "Here I am thinking you had some spicy information to tell me about a new lady love. On the other hand, Travis, I have to tell you she didn't seem at all your type."

A corner of his mouth quirked sardonically.

"She seemed awfully young."

Yes, he remembered clearly that she was. And there had been other things about her, as well.

"Anyway, I told her she could wait for you, but she said it wasn't important." Melinda folded away the Formica table and deck chairs, moving around Travis and now ignoring his atrophied expression, the bright green eyes eerie in the sunlight.

"Then I suppose it wasn't," Travis murmured tightly, his jaw tensing almost angrily. But Meinda didn't really hear him and didn't see the anger. And Travis went back to cleaning the fish.

Chapter Six

The gentle clicking of the typewriter keys filled the room, filled her head, blocking out thoughts, images and feelings. Her eyes flickered briefly back and forth from her written notes to the page in the carriage of the electric machine and from there to the square keys on which the slightest touch miraculously produced evenly printed letters. The letters eventually formed words and sentences that, she hoped, would make sense to someone.

This part of Cathy's creative writing could almost have been done by rote, typing legibly what she'd already thought out and written in longhand. Cathy had written an essay about motherhood. It had been Elizabeth Harris's idea.

When the older woman had returned from her meeting, it was with relief that she'd read the two phone messages left for her from Catherine Donnelly. Elizabeth, much attuned to that segment of Cathy's emotions that cried silently for support and understanding, had returned the calls and arranged for Cathy to see her as soon as possible.

On top of her traumatic return to Key West, waiting three days for Elizabeth to return to Miami had just about done Cathy in. Her anguish, loneliness, hurt, confusion and fears had all overwhelmed her, not allowing her to eat or sleep well. When she finally walked into Elizabeth's office and the door was closed, Elizabeth had softened completely, her eyes taking in the sad state of the younger woman. The instincts she had the very first time she'd ever seen Cathy were given full rein, and not a word was spoken as she opened her arms and Cathy came into them, holding on and crying her heart out.

And so it was that after more than three hours Elizabeth

came to know about Cathy and her life growing up over-protected by her father and older brother, about her growing up without benefit of a mother, about what Cathy thought her life would be like now that she was on her own. And after nearly that much time again, Cathy told Elizabeth all about Travis and how they'd met. Finally, Cathy had croaked out tearfully that he was already married, with children.

At first, Elizabeth expressed no opinions and gave no advice at all. She just asked a few questions and made mental notes of the answers. The last question Elizabeth asked had been a pointed "Do you want an abortion?"

Cathy's great dark eyes had looked steadily at the other woman. "I don't think I can do that. I—I know I'm afraid. I don't know what kind of mother I'm going to make, but I have to try."

Elizabeth had been surprised at the solidity of the answer. She'd half expected a tirade against a man named Travis, about duplicity and infidelity, about accidents and mistakes. But Cathy had involved no one else but herself in her decision. That was a positive sign.

And then Elizabeth had done what had seemed to Cathy two strange things. She'd first insisted that Cathy keep two appointments with a counselor so that it would be clear to the administration of the center that she understood her decision to keep the baby. And second, Elizabeth had asked her to write an essay, anonymously if she preferred, on what motherhood meant to her. She wanted to include it in a newsletter printed up for women registered at the center who'd have to grapple with the question of pregnancy, birth and motherhood or abortion.

Cathy had gratefully accepted the challenge, nodding silently to the older woman and watching a pleased smile soften Elizabeth's brown angular features. Her decision, however, did absolutely nothing to ease her hurt or the memory of Travis from her mind. Even her conclusion that Travis was already married and had children did not elicit hate in her for him—only disappointment. There was the absurd and probably childish revelation that he was a mere man, and mortal, after all, capable of mistakes and indiscretions. That it would cost her dearly for years to come if not for the rest of her life she did not even measure against her hopes for what she'd truly wished he would have been: someone who would have brought a kind of daring and magic to her otherwise safe, predictable life; her own hero, bigger than life, and more real than Brian, who was solid and normal. A normal relationship had never been all that exciting. Her heart ached for the strange emotional affinity she'd felt in those short twenty-four hours she'd spent with Travis. Cathy now believed they could have taught each other much.

Cathy had not realized she'd stopped typing. She blinked as she saw she'd overshot her margins and would have to either redo the page or erase the last four lines. Sighing softly in exasperation, she turned off the typewriter. She noticed now that with the setting sun it was growing dark in the apartment, and she switched on a desk lamp. Holding up a corner of the page, Cathy went over her words.

For the most part Cathy was pleased with what she'd written, considering she could hardly be thought knowledgeable on the subject. It was hard for her to define a mother because she'd not had one herself for very long. It was almost impossible to say who these women were, to themselves and to their children, because she'd long since given up wondering and never needed to know. Were mothers like other women? Did the fact that they were mothers preclude being anything else? Was a mother anything like herself, still curious and growing and questioning, or had all the questions already been answered? Suddenly, Cathy wished desperately that her own mother was there to talk to.

It just seemed to her, however, that being a mother had to be tied in to more than just a literal translation of the word and more than the physical act of giving birth. Didn't it also have to do with how one felt about just being a woman and a person? For that matter, what did being a *woman* mean?

Cathy sighed again, sipping from the glass of milk that stood next to her typewriter. She grimaced upon discovering it was almost warm. At the same time, a sharp twist of pain momentarily passed through her lower abdomen. She laid a slender hand flat to her stomach, wishing the cramps would stop. Elizabeth said they would, but Cathy had yet to return to the center for the rest of her examination since deciding against the abortion.

Her hand rubbed in a gentle circle on her stomach, and Cathy looked down at the motion, wondering abstractedly what was going on in there. Since finding out she was pregnant, she found it hard to actually visualize a baby. In her mind she imagined a small boxed space in her stomach where a change of some kind was taking place. In her mind, too, the space was dark and liquid with an unformed center. The cramps somehow seemed tied in to that murky center. The thought of an abortion left her sad. The thought of having a baby left her frightened, but it was a fear she would fight to overcome.

When there was a loud thumping knock on her apartment door, Cathy slowly got up from her long, narrow desk in front of the wide living-room windows and walked to answer, taking another hesitant sip from the tepid milk. The window in her bedroom had been stuck shut since she'd first moved in, making sleep in the overly warm room uncomfortable and sticky. The superintendent had been promising to fix it for a few weeks. It was too much to hope that on this very warm and humid June day he'd finally gotten around to it.

He hadn't. When Cathy opened the door, it was not short, stubby, cigar-smoking Mr. Nagler who stood before her but a fairly tall, dark man. His face was strongly chiseled and compellingly masculine. For a man, his cheekbones seemed a bit too prominent, as was his jaw. The chin was square. He was clean-shaven, although the shadow of his beard was discernible. His mouth was wide and sensually full but at the moment was more a hard, straight line, making him appear almost cruel. As Cathy finished examining his features, his jaw began to tense and untense rigidly, and only as her eyes rose to meet his did the question of his identity become clear.

There was much about Travis's face that had remained hidden when Cathy had first met him. But for as long as she lived, she'd always remember those eyes. Sad sea-green eyes, with cloudy gray flecks throughout. Cathy stood absolutely mesmerized, her heart beginning to thud painfully in her chest. The milk glass slipped from her limp fingers and shattered on the floor at her feet. Cathy paid no heed, her wide dark eyes riveted on the man in front of her.

"I suppose that means you're surprised to see me," Travis said dryly. He stepped over the mess into the apartment and closed the door behind him. Cathy silently stared at him and took two stumbling steps backward.

An emotion—something like surprised wonder, fleeting joy, apprehension, terror—chased across her face, brightening her eyes unnaturally.

Travis looked down at her bare feet and the broken glass but saw that she had not been cut. He looked back coldly to her face. "You do seem to have a talent for losing your grip on things," he said scathingly, and watched her face go instantaneously pale; she looked as if she'd just been hit. Impatiently, Travis looked over her shoulder. Locating the kitchen, he moved in that direction. Cathy finally came to life and started to follow.

Travis stopped short in his tracks and shot her a glance over his own shoulder. "Don't move!" he fairly thundered at her. "Just stay right there!" And Cathy, stunned by the angry command in his voice, stopped at once.

Travis returned seconds later with her yellow sponge from the sink and a handful of paper toweling. Hunching down on the balls of his feet, knees spread, he carefully soaked up the spilled milk and used the towels to gather the broken pieces of glass. Then his actions became less sharp and jerky, and he looked up at her again. Cathy was standing stone still, afraid to move, looking at him as if he were an apparition. And also, for a mere instant, perhaps they were both remembering the night of the storm when she'd dropped another vessel.

The anger that Travis had let burn within him for four days began to fade slowly now that he actually stood before her again. He held the wet mess in his hands and stood up straight, looking Cathy over slowly. He'd almost forgotten how little she seemed. He'd almost forgotten the dark glossy curls and how they framed a face that looked much too innocent, obviously, even for her own good. And there were the almost-black eyes that were bright as buttons and like bottomless pools, drawing him into their soft warm depths. His eyes swept over her slender body, dressed in a pair of white wide-legged shorts, making it appear like a very short skirt, worn with a pale blue tank top with narrow straps. It was evident to Travis that she wore no bra. But her breasts were well formed, and his quick assessment and memory told him that she didn't need one.

Cathy had not missed his close scrutiny of her or the way his eyes lingered on her breasts, pressed against the cotton fabric of her top. She was normally uncomfortable without a bra, but just lately her breasts were so tender and sensitive to the touch that it hurt to wear one. And with Travis's close examination of her came the image clear as day of his stroking her breasts. Cathy crossed her arms in front of her body self-consciously and shivered.

Except for the stormy eyes, Travis was like an entirely different person to her, the most startling difference being the absence of the beard. Cathy had thought him an attractive man with his beard. He was equally attractive without it. The realization brought sudden color back to her hollow cheeks. Travis was wearing a crisp white shirt, sharply contrasting with his sun-browned skin. Three buttons were open down the front, and the sleeves were rolled almost to his elbows. His tan trousers were low on his hips, emphasizing his lithe, hard build and long, muscled legs. Cathy also noticed a chocolate-brown duffel, discarded near the door when he'd first come in, with a brown suede sports jacket thrust through the strap handles. She came back to his intent, cold eyes.

"Wh-what are you doing here?" she asked simply, her voice more steady than she thought it would be. "How... did you find me?"

Travis paused another moment and then walked back to the kitchen around her. He tossed the sponge in the sink and threw the wad of paper toweling into the garbage.

Cathy frowned and slowly followed behind him. Travis turned to lean against the sink and crossed his arms over his firm chest.

"Finding you was a royal pain," he said, his voice and tone still hard but no longer angry. "I think I must have called every apartment-leasing agency in Miami and every major bank. I figured you had to have an account with someone here."

Cathy was amazed at his ingenuity; nonetheless, indignation made her chin rise. "They shouldn't have told you anything. That's all confidential information!"

Travis raised a dark wicked brow. "I didn't think they'd believe I was your brother," he said, flicking his eyes suggestively up and down her length. "So I told them you were a runaway wife."

Cathy's mouth dropped open. "You didn't!" she said, incredulous.

"I did!" he replied without hesitation. Then he stood straight, bracing his hands on his hips and allowing his voice to drop. His eyes grew darker and somehow very dangerous in their intensity. His jaw muscles worked. "And I think you know exactly why I'm here."

Cathy's neck and cheeks flushed pink. She placed a hand for support on the door frame of the kitchen. "I—I don't know why you're here. How could I?"

To Cathy it would seem obvious, however, that the blonde had said something to him. How could she not? Was she outraged and angry, hurt and bitter, that he could do something like this, making a mockery of their relationship? And to judge from Travis's cold anger with her, he obviously wasn't pleased that Cathy had tried to find him. She wished desperately now that she hadn't followed her instincts, which had led her back to Key West.

Travis looked thoughtfully at her, his eyes missing none of the emotions playing over her face. Nor did he miss now the drawn pinched look of her features or the fact that she seemed thinner than he remembered. When her hand suddenly went to her stomach, lying innocently against the flat surface, Travis's hands clenched tightly, and his eyes narrowed.

"I'd rather not discuss this standing in your kitchen. Can we at least sit down?" he asked softly, the tone low and deep. Cathy only nodded and turned reluctantly to pad barefoot into her living room, which also served as a dining area and her work studio.

She picked the least comfortable chair to sit on, then sat straight back, tense, on the edge of it. Travis first extracted a pack of cigarettes from his pants pocket and dropped gracefully to the more comfortable love seat, opposite Cathy. He lit a cigarette, keeping his eyes on her all the time, as if thinking over something, speculating or forming questions in his own mind. Travis exhaled a stream of smoke and leaned forward with his elbows on his knees.

"You're pregnant, aren't you." It was neither question nor statement.

Cathy's head jerked up sharply, and she stared at him, speechless. Her silence confirmed his thoughts.

"You...you're wrong. I—"

Travis smoothly interrupted her denials. "You came looking for me to tell me. I'm not sure if I'd have believed you then—abused dignity and offended sensibilities," he said sarcastically, "and all that. But having found where I was, you left again. Without saying a word."

"That doesn't mean anything," Cathy began again.

Travis was slowly shaking his head. "I don't believe you drove all the way back to Key West just to say thank you."

Cathy gnawed on her lip, seeing again the pretty blonde. "There—there was nothing more to say." But with her words, she inadvertently again added proof to Travis's speculations. She looked down at her fingers, twisting nervously together in her lap. "It—it was foolish to go back." Cathy shrugged helplessly. "I don't know why I did." Her cheeks were bright pink spots in a face that was still curiously pale.

Travis drew on his cigarette, squinting against the curling gray smoke. "Then it's pointless to ask if the baby's mine," he said without any change of expression.

Cathy's return of his intent gaze was unflinching, her chin lifting indignantly. "Totally pointless," she confirmed softly, her voice strong and steady. With insight she added, "And you wouldn't be here if you believed there was any doubt."

Their eyes held for a long minute, and it was Travis who finally broke the contact under the pretext of looking for an ashtray. Cathy silently got up, and emptying the paper clips from a shallow hand-crafted dish on her desk, gave it to him to use. Their fingers touched briefly. Hers were cold, his warm. They looked at each other again before Cathy took her seat.

Travis's brows drew together ominously, and he angrily flicked ashes from his cigarette into the dish. "I hope you're not in the habit of conducting, er, your relationships in this way," he said cruelly. Cathy stiffened and glared at him. Travis realized that he'd said an ugly thing. But his anger and frustration led him to want to test and push and hurt her, even as something inside said his first impression of her had not been wrong.

"That's an awful thing to say! There's only Brian. I—" Cathy stopped. One boyfriend or none at all. How could she justify this situation?

Travis raised a brow. "Brian?" He drew deeply on the cigarette. "He's still in for one hell of a surprise."

"He's not going to know. It—it's none of his business," Cathy said, but her voice was weakening again. The enormity of the situation was hitting her from so many different angles she hadn't considered before.

"Then you're not serious about his feelings, either. And I bet he was your high school sweetheart!" He smirked sarcastically.

Cathy paled again and frowned at his first reference. There wasn't any way to explain about Brian. "You don't understand!" she said helplessly. Why didn't he remember how she came to be in his arms in the first place, how she came to know him intimately? "This wasn't deliberate or—or careless." She gestured with her hands, words catching in her throat. "It—it just wasn't supposed to happen...." But it was doubtful that Travis heard her, or even if he did, that he would fully understand. Cathy's voice trailed off, and she glanced quickly at him.

But Travis's expression clearly stated that he was un-

sympathetic. Then, after a long silence, he let out a weary
sigh. Impatiently, he crushed the cigarette out. Travis
knew she wasn't the kind to sleep around. It was without
question that night he kept her in his bed. What had happened with him was obviously bad luck and poor timing.
But Travis couldn't ignore his own more glaring need at
the time of not wanting to be alone.

His stormy eyes lifted to follow Cathy as she suddenly
stood up again and walked to one of the large picture windows behind her desk. She'd taken the apartment because
of the windows. They looked out over Biscayne Bay and a
blue sky puffed with white clouds. Just as she'd imagined
Florida should be. But now the sky was getting dark and
sad.

"You don't have to worry. I—I won't ask anything of
you."

Travis grew alert. "What do you mean?"

Cathy kept her back to him. She hugged her stomach.
The cramps had returned. "Because of your family.
You're safe. Why—why should they suffer just because
you didn't think of their feelings!"

Travis got up and followed her to the window. "What
the hell has my family to do with this?" He grabbed her
arm roughly and pulled her around to face him.

"I—I didn't say anything to her—to Mrs. Hoyt!" Cathy
said quickly.

"Melinda?" Travis said incredulously, blinking at Cathy
in confusion.

Is that her name? Cathy thought dismally. "Haven't
they been hurt enough?" Cathy forced herself to look
into his face and couldn't keep the tears from welling or
blurring his image. "It's all right. There's nothing you
have to do or say." Her voice broke, and a few tears rolled
down her cheeks and past her quivering chin.

Travis frowned even more, searching her face, wonder-
ing at her meaning. What did she know of his family? Had
Melinda said more than she'd admitted to? Suddenly,
Cathy let out a short laugh, high-pitched and strange.
"This is just another nightmare you can forget about. Not
admit to—"

Travis shook her. "Stop it! You're getting hysterical."

Cathy now fought against his touch on her upper arms, the tears, along with her surprised shock, flowing freely. "I'm not hysterical! I—I'm just pregnant. I'm going to have a baby—your baby."

"Cathy! For heaven's sake—"

"No! I'm not going to have your baby!"

Travis muttered a curse and shook her again. Cathy's head snapped back sharply, and the sounds were immediately shut off as she stared blankly at him, her eyes large and shimmering with tears. Cathy bit her lip, forcing herself to control the hysteria, but quietly now she continued to cry. Travis watched her helplessly, all of his anger dissipating as he felt her slight body trembling under his hands. He gentled his hold and slowly urged her forward into his arms, even as she resisted.

"Don't—don't touch me," she croaked out thinly, her hands braced against his hard chest wall.

Once more Travis tensed his jaw, angry at her attempt to reject him. But the anger had less to do with Cathy than it did with his own memories and his own acknowledgment that what was happening now was most certainly his fault. "It's a little late to tell me that!" he said tightly, and despite Cathy's silent protest, he pulled her against him. Her forehead came forward to rest on his chest, and she sobbed quietly.

Travis felt awkward. He didn't know if he should stroke her or pet her or say something. Holding her now was so unlike that first time when the physical aura surrounding them had been distinctly sexual and intoxicatingly arousing, even in the comfort they gave each other at the time. Travis decided on stroking, his hands roaming hesitantly to feel and recognize that she'd lost weight since he'd last seen and held her.

"I don't suppose you've eaten anything today?" Travis asked, his voice still a little rough but at least not so cutting or angry.

Today? Not even yesterday as far as Cathy could remember. She shook her head, her forehead still pressed to his chest. Her nose got a whiff of his warm male body along with the clean, salt-air smell of his shirt. Cathy turned her head now to lay her cheek against his shirt-front. Travis's hand rose slowly up her back, rubbing comfortingly across her shoulders.

"I think you and I have a lot to get straight," Travis said, leading her to the love seat. "But first maybe you should eat something. You don't need to hear my stomach growl, and I don't need you in a dead faint!"

A curious dry laugh shook Cathy's shoulders at the unintended humor on his part. But Travis took it as a positive sign and left her to rummage through the kitchen. Cathy sat where he'd left her, unable to move and drained of her last energy. She didn't understand why he'd bother to try to find her. After all, what was there to be done or said at this point with the indisputable fact of Melinda and her children? What would possibly change with his coming, and how was it going to help her?

Cathy might have saved herself enormous anguish and time asking unanswerable questions had she been able to reason for herself that if Travis *was* married, the last thing he'd do was seek her out. And certainly if he was callous and irresponsible, as she now wanted to believe of him, he would have hardly bothered. Instead, Cathy sat in a daze for nearly an hour, ignoring the movements and sounds and smells from the kitchen, wondering what it was Travis wanted from her.

In the meantime, Travis was busy trying to develop another strategy for dealing with the situation. His immediate impression upon seeing Cathy again was that she was every bit as young as he remembered and very confused by what was happening to her. In view of her shock, his anger seemed terribly misplaced. And he didn't blame her for her response to him. He'd come on like a ton of bricks.

It wasn't until Travis brought out two hot plates from the kitchen and set them on her round butcher-block dining table that she blinked and came to life again. Silently, Cathy got up and got silverware and napkins from the kitchen. She poured glasses of apple juice to go with the meal, because that was all she had in the refrigerator to drink. Finally, they sat down to eat. Cathy was more herself now but looked rather warily up at Travis, then down to the plate in front of her. She found a sautéed fillet of flounder from a frozen pack in her freezer, buttered noodles and steamed carrots. Her throat went dry.

Travis sat down and looked hard at her, his angled face completely hiding from her his own concerns and anxieties. His eyes swept again over the curly head, the soft fluffy hair framing her pale face, the eyes so wounded and unsure, the mouth beautifully shaped and full—and sad. Dammit! She hadn't the first idea how to take care of herself, Travis thought, angry both at her and himself.

"Eat!" he ordered, waiting for Cathy to pick up the fork before beginning himself. There seemed to be nothing wrong with his appetite, and Cathy watched in a kind of fascinated, hypnotic horror as he bit into a succulent piece of the fish. By the same token, Cathy's movements in eating were almost in slow motion. The fork seemed to weigh a ton. She lowered her eyes to the plate, watching the buttery juices of the sauce run from the fish and make a yellow liquid circle around it.

Cathy heard Travis's voice, heard him say something totally irrelevant about her being too thin, that starving was a stupid way to kill herself, and that the sauce would have been thicker if he'd added more flour. The food was tasteless in her mouth.

But then something strange began to happen. His deep voice seemed to slow and slur like a record played at the wrong speed. Her body was swept from head to toe in a sudden wave of heat that was at once followed by a chilly clamminess to her skin. Cathy could feel the goose bumps at about the same time her stomach started to churn and tumble and heave in protest. Little prickly white dots began to float on her plate, or did it only seem that way? Sweat broke out on her forehead, and a humming started in her ears. Why were there bells ringing? And why was the fish swimming before her eyes when it was supposed to be cooked?

The next thing Cathy knew, Travis had her out of her seat, and she found herself being propelled blindly around the table and into the bathroom. She knew she couldn't have walked there on her own. Not when she only wanted to lie down and die peacefully.

Cathy was forced inelegantly to her knees in front of the bathroom bowl. A hand was firmly and with resolve pushed to the back of her head, holding it down while her insides rumbled up and out. Travis was murmuring to her, very soothing and understanding even as the hand kept her head down, his other hand holding her gently around the waist. All Cathy could think of was how much a blessing it would be never to eat again—to lie down, close her eyes and have the world go away.

Travis kept his hold around her middle and with the other hand now moistened a washcloth in the sink. Soon it was pressed to her forehead and cheeks and wiped across her trembling lips. Cathy couldn't open her eyes. She didn't want to. Now that everything had almost stopped spinning, she didn't want to do anything that would start it going again.

Cathy felt herself being slowly turned by the shoulders, her face pressed against a warm, hard surface covered in crisp summer cotton. She enjoyed the feel, the comforting strong arm, the whispered words into her hair. It felt as if she belonged there. Cathy lifted her head up, Travis tilted his down, and they looked at one another. Travis's eyes were searching and seemed curiously tender. The moment of discovery was frozen in silence. Eyes met eyes and examined earnestly. Cathy had imagined his eyes a cold sea-gray-green, but now they were just green.

Travis was noticing her creamy smooth skin, now very pale and quite cool to the touch. A finger absently traced along her cheek to the corner of her mouth. Her lips parted. Her mouth was pretty, he remembered, happy when she smiled, poutish when she frowned, sensual when she was thoughtful—like now.

"I—I'm sorry," Cathy suddenly voiced weakly.

Was she embarrassed? Travis wasn't sure. And he didn't care. His eyes turned a rich dark green. "So am I," he answered in a husky deep voice.

Travis started to stand up, pulling Cathy with him. He stooped and lifted her into his arms, and she lay helpless and exhausted against him as he carried her into the stifling bedroom, laying her gently on the bed. He could have left her like that, vulnerable and askew across the mattress. Her eyes were closed. Instead, Travis pulled her straight and cautiously began to unbutton the white shorts, maneuvering them down her hips and legs. For a moment he was mesmerized by her lower body, encased in a pair of lacy pink panties. Travis looked up to find Cathy's dark eyes trained on his face in a gaze that was both questioning and drowsy. She made no move to stop him.

Travis next reached to pull the blue top over her head, again alternately moving his eyes from his chore to her face to gauge a reaction. Cathy half aided him by attempting to lift her arms so it could slip off. Travis's jaw tensed as he now became transfixed by her breasts, by the deep rose of her nipples and their soft erectness. She was still merely watching him, her expression unchanged.

Finally, Travis pulled the bedspread up and over her, not bothering to move her again. He went to the window and with two strenuous shoves got the stubborn window open, and warm, humid Florida air breezed in to stir around the room. Cathy's eyes were closed again, and Travis watched her for a long moment. He experienced alternate anger and helplessness. He wished he had followed his original inclinations that night two months ago and sent her about her business in the rain. He wished she were older and more like all the women he'd known in brief moments of simple physical need and convenience. And although at first he'd wished she had just gone ahead and done what she thought best, he was now strangely moved by her stalwart determination to handle her pregnancy on her own and hold him blameless.

Cathy was fast asleep. With a great deal of emotion, lost to the quiet room, Travis ran his hand through his hair. "I'm sorry..." He sighed again deeply, feeling that he always seemed to be saying that to someone. He never meant to hurt anyone or disappoint anyone. But somehow he always did.

Chapter Seven

Travis took one last drag on the cigarette, finishing it. Then, concentrating with an effort that was heroic, he managed to put out the butt, without spilling any of the contents, in an ashtray that was already overflowing.

"I'll have another," Travis said stiffly, gesturing toward his empty glass. Was it his eighth, tenth or twelfth drink? He'd lost count, and so had the bartender. But since Travis didn't give any particular outward signs of being drunk, there was no reason in the bartender's mind not to allow him to finish the bottle of gin he'd started with earlier in the evening. At two dollars a shot what did he care if his customer was intent on pickling his liver? But if Travis had been down in Key West, Joe would have packed him off home five drinks ago.

The fact of the matter was, although in the morning his head would feel like the hollow underside of a clanging gong, Travis's liver would be fine. He was not a drinker. He only drank to excess when the need for isolation led him to the easy and ready oblivion of a liquor bottle. For a night or a day the confusion in his head would float on the liquid stimulus, separating into little corners of his mind, and then eventually it would appear clearly to him, and if it was a problem of some kind, a solution might even present itself. Of course, an additional side effect was the lingering bad taste of alcohol, remorse and the fervent vow never to drink so heavily again.

Travis had found his way to the dim and unattractive place with very little trouble. He reasoned dryly to himself that he had a talent for finding the seamy side of life, or it found him, when he wasn't thinking very highly of himself. He'd certainly felt less than terrific as he'd stood by Cathy's bed, watching her pale, damp features, with its defenselessness, knowing he was responsible for her state. He should have known better. At thirty-five, he'd been around long enough to be able to detect potential trouble. But Cathy was not someone you just walked away from. He would always wonder if she was okay. In any case, the way things had turned out, Travis wouldn't have walked away even if he'd wanted to. Instead, he'd just walked far enough to get drunk.

And Travis was also most selective. He only indulged in such destructive behavior when there was a crisis at hand. The first time had been at the age of nineteen, after a blowout argument with his father, who'd threatened to disown him. It had been a regular threat through most of his teens when his father, founder and owner of one of the East Coast's largest and most reliable sea salvaging companies, had begun to school Travis and his older brother, Mitchell, to take over the family business. But Travis had not wanted to follow in his father's considerable footsteps; he had wanted to blaze his own trails.

Travis wanted to fly. The battle raged hot and heavy all the time he trained as an aviator and graduated as an officer from the Air Force Academy. It took a brief reprieve as Travis flew missions during the last three years of the Vietnamese conflict. And although Travis was hotheaded enough not to believe it then, his family just wanted him to come home alive, no matter what he wanted to do with his life. When his father had been confined to moving by canes and crutches because of a company-related accident, it had been his oldest son, Mitchell, who'd been on hand to take over. That served to take a lot of pressure off Travis when he returned to the Boston area to start his life anew. But his absence had barely mended the deep rent in the fragile fabric of his relationship with his father. While his mother was alive, the gap frequently could be bridged for long periods of family harmony. That is, until the clash of wills between father and son started again, sending Travis off to some adventure until he could cool down.

What had most pained Travis, however, was that he knew he was exactly like his father in many ways—fearless to the point of foolishness, stubborn and capable of drawing immovable lines. They both possessed tempers that were quick to explode; but they were equally quick to forgive. But there was also the generous nature they shared, a sense of the ridiculous, leading them both to take very little seriously. But when you had either's attention or love, you had it forever. It had always hurt and frustrated Travis that he couldn't have been on better terms with his father. He loved him deeply and respected him even more for what he had made of himself.

It had been hard to watch Mitch take over the company, however, not out of any sense of jealousy or sibling rivalry but because Mitch had no head for business. Give Mitch something to do and it could be safely left to him to see it through, all the little details covered. But asking Mitch to take the initiative, make decisions logically, was futile. He was an excellent follower but no leader. Leading, taking charge, taking risks, had always been Travis's forte, like his father's. And even in his worst moments, if he was around, he could be counted on.

The second time Travis had gotten drunk had also been after a heated argument. He'd left home in a fury, only to return three days later married to a young woman he'd just met. It had been a disastrous mistake that cost him dearly, not the least of which was eighteen months of his life spent with a less than stimulating brunette who had little to say for herself and even less to recommend her. But she had been fantastic in bed, rounding out that portion of his education.

Oddly, it was she who finally wanted out, when it became clear that Travis, who certainly had the financial means, was not interested in providing her with the finer things in life. She had been able to do that for herself from a rather healthy divorce settlement. Her name had been Cathy, too....

Travis downed the fresh drink quickly, its bitter, nerve-jolting taste knocking some of his foolish past right out of his head. But not all of it. His early adventures had certainly been colorful, and unbeknownst to him, his father often had a good hearty laugh over his son's strong individualism and inventiveness. Travis was purely a younger version of himself.

No, the parts that couldn't be dismissed with a wry shrug of the shoulder had hit more rawly to his heart and guts, making him wonder if his father had indeed been right all those times he'd ranted in anger that he, Travis, would end up in hell yet. For hell it surely was that he'd experienced after the crash in which Mitch had been killed.

It had been after the divorce from Cathy, and Travis had made a last effort, with good intentions and determination, to be the kind of son his father wanted him to be. He'd been offered a flying post with the U.S. Weather Service but had turned it down to go, at last, into the family business.

Travis had used his aviation ability to aid in the location and area clearance of salvage sites. It was a concession his father grudgingly accepted in lieu of his son's actually sitting behind a desk. Travis himself was adjusting and settling in to the inevitability of the situation when final tragedy struck.

The company had gotten an emergency call from the construction team of an offshore oil-drilling rig; equipment had been lost off the site into the sea and was needed to finish the present phase of work. Travis had asked Mitch to get a layout of the rig above and below sea level and where all present equipment was placed. He'd also relied on Mitch to have the plane checked out for the flight while he himself readied an aerial camera for pictures. All had gone as planned until they circled the site for the last time and headed toward the shore. A red light began to blink on the dash, indicating lack of oil and engine malfunction. The right engine started to choke and sputter, smoke emitting from the dry motion until the engine stopped completely and the plane began to dip.

Travis was forced to fly farther afield to avoid any crowded areas in case he had to let down. The plane flew with just one engine, but it, too, began to lose rotation power, and the dipping and banking became more erratic and dangerous. Travis cut the engines almost completely, hoping to glide and slowly drop the plane down on one of a series of flat deserted piers on the shoreline. And drop she did, skidding and sparking toward the end of the pier. Travis drove the throttle to the side sharply, bringing the tail of the plane swinging around. But the right wing also swung and slammed into the side of a cement building, and the troubled engine burst into flames.

Mitch was knocked half-conscious, trapped in his seat as flames licked into his side of the plane. Travis released the safety belts on both of them, an awful piercing pain shooting up one arm, but he couldn't budge his brother's helpless body. Travis's hands got badly burned in the effort until the pain and blisters made them useless.

The sirens sounded from afar, and Travis worked his way out of the plane to get help. He could hear Mitch coming around, yelling not to leave him, to help him out, too. Travis looked at his hands, now blistered to twice their size, the skin singed and peeled back.

"I can't Mitch! Hold on. I'll get help!"

"Please, Travis, don't leave me! Get me out! It's hot...it's burning..."

"Oh, God, Mitch..."

Then there was that awful scream as flames finally consumed the cabin. Travis had yelled his brother's name, and nearly passing out with the pain, had started back to get him. But someone tackled him from behind to the ground and held him there as he struggled and watched Mitchell die.

Hours later he could hear Mitch scream. Years later he could still hear it. It still came to him in the night while he slept. It was his own fault, not Mitch's. He was at fault, because a good pilot never relies on anyone for the final checkout of his plane. Travis could still hear, still see himself coming to in the hospital, one arm in a bubble splint up to his shoulder, both arms and hands smeared with salve, telling his brother that he would get him out. He could still see the ashen, stiff-faced look of his father, the eyes glassy and blank—indifferent, Travis always felt. After all these years...

That had been nearly four years ago, and he hadn't been back home since.

Travis pushed the glass aside and fished for yet another cigarette. He thought with a wry bit of humor that he must be developing a tolerance for gin. He still felt too clear-headed. The images of the past were too precise. It couldn't just be that he was getting used to the past. You never get used to the things that haunt you. He let out a deep exhalation of gray smoke into the already-smoky air. The bartender automatically refilled the glass and silently walked away. Travis propped his bristled cheek into the heel of the hand with the cigarette and contemplated the drink with a frown.

And now there was Cathy. Travis had been staring into another drink in the tavern on Key West when her soft, shy voice had broken the old alcoholic air of the room. In all honesty, he hadn't remembered too much else about her that night. He'd talked with her for a time, and then she had left. She'd looked rather like a wet cat, huddled along the side of the building, shivering when he'd found her again. And he recognized that she was young—god-awful young, he had thought in exasperation at the time. But she did have this soft, low voice, feminine and silky, and incredible curly hair.

It wasn't until the next day, when he was almost clear-headed again and he'd come in from shopping to find her up and awake and rosy-cheeked from sleep, that he saw she was no teenager but a young woman. Travis had been surprised and then amused by her lack of concern over the dangerous awkwardness of their night alone together. He had been too tired to make advances the night before. But there had been nothing to stop him that next day— except that it was obvious she trusted him and felt safe with him.

Cathy herself had been so honest and open, so obviously unexposed to much, although he wasn't sure just how inexperienced. When he'd kissed her, she was hesitant, but she knew how to respond. There was much about her that was the mature developed woman and much that was the unknowing adolescent tease. She had been a puzzle to him. He was never sure when to just pat her on the head or sweep her into his arms and cart her off to his bedroom. And not being sure, Travis tried to leave her alone, but it had been hard.

For one thing, it had been an age since Travis had met someone so fresh and appealing. His life recently had been conducted with a deliberate effort to avoid serious involvement, believing that he still had a penchant for hurting people. Many women came in and out of his life. They were attractive, often beautiful, understood what he did and did not want, and kept their association brief and to the point. He neither needed or wanted anything from them beyond that.

Melinda, his sister-in-law, was virtually the only platonic relationship he maintained. Travis saw her more as a sister, someone he really liked and respected and someone who accepted him just as he was. And if he sometimes slipped, imagining a real relationship with someone he could love, he only had to recall that he'd deprived Melinda and her two sons the benefit of an attentive husband and good father for the urge to go away.

And that was mostly how it had been. Until Cathy. Never had any of his women companions been witness to his nightmares. And if they had, not by word, gesture or action did they let it be known to him. And never had any of them tried to comfort and soothe him, their voices filled with real concern and compassion. Only Cathy had done that. She had taken his panic seriously and had been willing to let herself be used as a sounding board for airing it if he'd let her. Cathy had nonplussed him, confused him and almost made a believer out of him again in goodness and love. Yes, most certainly love.

Travis's brows drew together in a deep frown of memory. He hadn't meant to drag her into bed with him that second night. But it was almost as if twenty-four hours of her wide-eyed curiosity and trust had loosened some ties on his needs, and he didn't want to be alone anymore. It was heavenly to have a soft, lithe female body pressed against him that neither asked nor demanded anything of him. But he had wanted and demanded much from her.

Travis had wanted to make her real to him. He had wanted to press into her flesh deeply and surround himself in her compassion and care and innocence for more than just a quick climax. He had wanted to give of himself this once, because he didn't do it often. Giving had a tendency to leave him feeling too vulnerable. He had wanted to take from Cathy part of her youth and softness and the responding appeal of her body.

He should have guessed she was a virgin. He should have seen it in her eyes, which always gave so much of her away. But he hadn't been thinking much of her feelings. When he'd first thrust into her soft body, unprepared for the resistance and too quickly forcing past it, her fingers had dug into his shoulders, and a long moan had escaped. But she hadn't cried out. Travis had collapsed on her, holding himself in surprised stillness.

"Oh, Cathy! Why didn't you say something!" Travis had growled hoarsely. "It didn't have to hurt this way!" And he had tried holding her closer and more gently. After interminable minutes Cathy moved her head against his shoulder and attempted to lift her hips.

"Travis?" Cathy had called his name faintly. He came up on his elbows to look down at her face. Her eyes were sparkling and black in their centers, her breathing was a little hurried, the air warm on his then hair-covered chin. A tear ran from her eye down her cheek into her hairline, but she wasn't crying. It had been forced out by the momentary pain she hadn't fully expected. "Travis..." she whispered again, a soft, slender hand moving up to his neck to circle it.

Travis was spellbound by her warmth and hesitant urging. He relaxed and kissed her eyes closed. "I'll be careful. I promise not to hurt you again."

And after that he hadn't, although she couldn't help being somewhat tender in places, even when his own need had taken over virilely, making Cathy thoroughly aware of every nuance of his passion and of him physically. He had been overwhelming. And she had been too caught up in the wonder of him pressed to her to feel she'd missed anything as he finished and lay damp and exhausted on top of her. Curling up next to him minutes later in a daze, Cathy had gone to sleep.

When he'd awakened her later in the night, anxious to sample her loveliness again, he had been able to initiate her to the ecstasy that he had known, delighting in her new responses, because they were happening for the first time with him. Cathy had been so totally accepting, learning to move with him, holding him. Her skin had been like velvet, her mouth soft and accessible to the exploration of his tongue. Travis had meant it when he'd whispered, "It would be so easy to love you." The words had slipped out spontaneously but nonetheless were true. So his surprise had been startling upon waking the next morning and finding her gone. Then he began to question whether it had all really happened. Or had she just materialized for a while to save his sanity and his soul? But Travis had found her red bandanna and knew relief that she had existed—and regret that she'd fled.

Cathy had persisted in his thoughts beyond reason. For one thing, she had left him a legacy of peaceful nights for nearly a month without his tormenting nightmare and days of persisting speculation as to what might have developed between them. To have found her as he had, by chance both two months ago and now, was responsible for his current state of intoxication. It had been too much to hope for and too much to believe that he had. And Travis hadn't even counted the one time he'd made a hesitant attempt to find her, knowing only her name and that she was somewhere in Miami. He'd felt like a fool, wandering the streets just hoping to see her and angry beyond reason when he didn't. He'd been angry that she'd left so much behind, and yet almost nothing at all. It left him in a kind of limbo, and sometimes at night, when he was alone with the dream, it bordered on purgatory.

Travis had been thankful for the one assignment that had kept him busy for nearly five weeks in Southern California and Mexico. But it had not completely cleared his mind of her. She was little more than a girl, but he had responded to the youthful, wide-eyed vitality like to a lifeline.

Now he could see that the naiveté was gone. He had done that. Her eyes were no less curious when they looked at him, but they were certainly more wary and alert. Travis had reacted angrily at finding out she was pregnant, not at her but because he would have wanted it to have happened differently. But at least he had found her, and that was a start.

"It's almost two A.M., buddy. I don't know about you, but I'm going home. I suggest you do the same." The bartender took the once-again empty glass, the brimming ashtray, and put them away. He began turning out lights and motioning toward the door. "You do have a home, don't ya, buddy?"

Travis carefully got off the stool, grunted and walked in a credible straight line to the door. Yeah, he had a home. And it was time he thought of returning to it. People die for want of a second chance. For forgiveness, restitution, recovery, rebirth. Travis knew that through Cathy he could have that chance. He wasn't sure how yet, but he believed it. He wasn't even sure what he had to offer Cathy. Support, himself, love—whatever. He just hoped she would accept it.

CATHY JUMPED AWAKE at the thumping on the door. Her heart raced momentarily in her startled body. My God, was that Mr. Nagler? She looked around in confusion. A cool night breeze blew through her open bedroom window. She frowned. Had Mr. Nagler already been there and fixed the window?

The thumping started again. Cathy turned on the adjustable reading lamp attached to the wall over her bed. She looked down in surprise to find she had no clothes on except for pink panties, and she'd fallen asleep on top of the bed. Cathy looked at the clock. It was three-fifteen in the morning, and she had no idea what had happened the night before. She absently brushed back the hair from her eyes as her stomach grumbled and roared, and she moved to find a robe. She felt light-headed and dizzy. Cathy supposed she hadn't eaten dinner, but for some reason she remembered fish floating in a lemon butter sauce! Suddenly, Cathy gasped, blinked rapidly in memory, hastily pulled on a yellow velour robe and ran to the door.

The remains of the dinner were gone, but Travis's duffel was still by the door, and from the persistent pounding she guessed now where Travis was. Cathy opened the self-locking door to confront him. Her eyes widened in shock.

"I'm new in town," Travis quipped in a husky slur, swaying a bit on his feet. "I can't get back to Key West and I have no place to stay."

Cathy continued to stare at him even as she blushed in memory of the circumstances that had forced her to remain for two nights in Key West. A foolish grin flashed over his tired, scruffy face, making Travis look wicked under the darkened beard growth.

"But at least it's not raining!"

Cathy came out of her astonished state and, grabbing his arm, pulled him into her apartment and quickly closed the door. "Travis! You're drunk! What on earth have you been doing?"

"Drinking," he supplied helpfully. Travis turned to face her, his movements a clear indication that his vision of her swayed before him. "Cathy," he began in a very serious voice, clamping his large hands heavily on her small shoulders, "I'm going to stay to help you."

"Oh, Travis," Cathy said sadly, looking into his bloodshot green eyes. "You can't help me. You can't help anyone right now!"

"But I—I want to," Travis got out jerkily.

Cathy made a sound of exasperation and began trying to maneuver him toward the bedroom. "Well, I don't need your help, thank you. I can manage by myself.... Not there, Travis. That's a closet! Watch where you're going!"

Cathy had him standing finally by the bed, but then she stood in hesitation, gnawing her lip.

"I'm staying, anyway," Travis said firmly, with momentary clarity.

"You'll feel differently in the morning!" Cathy said caustically. Making a decision at last, Cathy straightened her back and reached with resolve for the belt on Travis's slacks. He stood passive and unaware as she got the pants unzipped and began moving them down his muscular legs and thighs. She couldn't help swallowing in awareness herself, nor could she stop the sudden vision of his hips thrusting against her own in passion. Cathy could feel the heat of a deeper blush covering her face, neck and ears, and she now felt hot all over.

Cathy felt Travis's fingers gently in her hair.

"Cathy," Travis said quietly, his voice deep and earnest, "why did you leave?"

Cathy's head jerked up, and they looked at each other. For a moment she believed the question was real, and she opened her mouth to answer. But Travis's attention wandered again, and Cathy swallowed her answer. Angry that he'd not given her a chance to respond and that he might not really care, Cathy gave him a firm push on his chest, and he went backward. Travis's legs against the side of the bed caused him to sit suddenly and heavily on the edge of the mattress. With more vigor than was really needed, Cathy removed his shoes and then yanked off the pants and tossed them in disgust on the floor. Travis and his clothing reeked of liquor, tobacco and smoke.

Next she reached for the shirt buttons. But Travis noticed her again and with another grin reached drunkenly for her. Cathy pushed his arms away impatiently as he tried to hug her and quickly unbuttoned his shirt.

"You're sweet," Travis said with a smile. "I've never met anyone like you."

"I can believe that!" Cathy said dryly, pushing the shirt over his shoulders. The action brought her head close to his.

"You have a beautiful mouth," Travis observed, and then, surprising her with his quickness and strength, pulled Cathy between his legs and against his naked chest. Travis reached to kiss her with anything but drunken fervor. Cathy was first stiff with shock. Then, with a moan, she quickly went limp in response, remembering and enjoying and succumbing to the delicious, expert manipulations of his mouth and tongue, not for an instant minding the taste of gin. But then she garbled a protest and pulled out of his reach.

"Stop that!" Cathy said in a breathless voice.

"Didn't you like it?" he asked blandly, but she ignored him and her traitorous urge to have him kiss her again. Cathy got the shirt off, leaving Travis sitting in his shorts.

She removed his socks as Travis all the while continued his drunken dissertation on unrelated topics, asking abstract, unclear questions and again stating his determination to stay with her. Cathy only got madder at him, wondering how he could so readily forget Melinda and the kids. *Fool!* she cursed herself. *Of course he'd forget. Isn't that how your major problem began?*

All at once Cathy was feeling exhausted again. She was also surprisingly hungry but didn't have the strength or the inclination to go find anything now. Also, she was starting to feel depressed.

"Cathy..."

She looked at him. His face was so weary. So strong and handsome. He seemed serious again. "What?"

Travis took her hands in his own, his eyes trying hard to stay focused and centered. "There's...so much I have to tell you. So much...you don't know or understand. I'm not a rotten person, taking advantage of—of people."

It was a startling declaration coming from him, considering his state. "I—I believe you, Travis," Cathy replied softly, wanting to. He put a hand to his head and squeezed his eyes closed.

"Dammit! If only...my head would stop ringing. I can't think straight!"

Cathy sighed. "Then why don't you go to sleep. It will feel better in the morning."

He looked at her, almost boyishly now, his eyes soft and clouded. "You promise?"

Cathy couldn't help smiling at him. In an instinctive gesture, she brushed a hand over his ruffled dark hair and began to urge him to lie down. "I promise."

Agreeably, and with a sigh, Travis stretched out, closed his eyes for a final time and was asleep. Cathy stood watching his total open vulnerability of the moment and wondered about the man. Two days in his company had obviously given her very little knowledge of Travis. She'd come away with an intimate, highly personal part of him, but knowing him was much more complicated. She wished he could stay. She wished she could believe that in the morning when he was sober he'd have all the answers. But even her omnipotent Greek heroes, who were half gods themselves, weren't that clever.

Travis rolled over onto his stomach, and one muscled arm dropped heavily over the side of the bed to hang toward the floor. Cathy left him like that. She didn't know where she was going to sleep but finally reasoned that in his present condition she was safest with him. Throwing the bedspread over him, Cathy took off the robe, slid carefully under the top sheet, and allowing herself only twelve inches on the very edge of the bed, in exhaustion went back to sleep.

Travis slept like the dead and to some extent felt that way. But he was brought back from deep sleep, reluctantly, by an excruciating tingling sensation in his left arm. It felt numb, as though the fingers had fallen off. Grimacing painfully, he forced one heavy-lidded eye open and slowly turned his head, somehow expecting to find the arm missing from the shoulder down. What Travis found instead was Cathy fast asleep next to him. He had no clear idea where he was at the moment, how he got there or how she did. But she was curled on her side toward him and was using his forearm as a pillow.

Travis tried clenching his numb hand closed, and the effort made his jaw tense. The circulation had been cut, and he was very uncomfortable. Yet he was hesitant about making her move. Slowly, Travis worked his arm loose, Cathy's head dropping gently onto the actual pillow between them. Half sitting up, Travis bent and flexed the limb, which felt like a limp noodle, and got the blood flowing and the kinks worked out.

More or less awake now, if not alert, Travis looked down and studied his bedmate. Cathy's head was a riot of dark springy soft curls. And her curled-up, cozy body somehow reminded Travis of a cat or, rather, a soft fluffy

kitten. Absently, he reached out to carelessly brush a few
strands of her hair with his hand and then to wind a length
around his finger, watching it gently corkscrew back into
place as he pulled the finger free. Cathy moved, snuggling
down farther into the linens. The bedspread that covered
him was all tangled in the sheet that covered her. Travis
now found himself on the edge of the bed, and Cathy had
commandeered the center. Travis smiled ruefully in the
dark. Well, after all, it *was* her bed!

Travis carefully got off the bed and tried to stand, only
to find that the floor and walls were moving, and his head
felt heavy as a rock. But he managed to pull the linens
straight around Cathy's sleeping form, and then he got
back into the bed next to her. It was rather a tantalizing
shock to find her nearly naked. Somehow she seemed the
kind to sleep in a nightie, all covered and cute. And as
instantly appealing as he now found her the way she was,
he simply didn't have the strength to do anything about it.

Carefully, Travis tried to get his arm back around her,
trying to figure how to get her to use his shoulder rather
than his arm for sleeping on. But Cathy herself solved the
problem by stirring in her sleep, moving inadvertently toward Travis, her head finding his shoulder all by itself.
And thus, once again settled and comfortable, they both
passed a rather pleasurable summer's night in each other's
arms.

Travis awakened just after dawn. It was an automatic
reflex of a lot of fliers and sailors. His head that morning
felt as though a dozen loose marbles rolled around freely
in empty space. He gently disentangled himself from decidedly feminine limbs and curves, and careful that his
bedmate remained covered, got out of bed. He rubbed a
hand over the back of his neck and, with his eyes still
closed and his other hand stretched out before him for
guidance, went in search of the bathroom.

The cold shower water pelting his sleek, hard body a
minute later was miraculously reviving. Under its therapeutic stream the last vestiges of the previous night's
foray disappeared. Except for his head, and that could be
remedied with strong black coffee. It was only as he left

the bathroom in search of clothes that the surroundings settled into his consciousness, recalling to mind where he was and why. Sobering even more now, he swept his hands through his thick damp hair, moving to get his duffel and retrieving a pair of well-worn jeans. Then he went back to the open bedroom door.

Travis pushed one hand into a front pocket and leaned against the door frame. The other hand was braced on the doorknob. His jaw tensed, and his eyes grew dark green and probing as he looked at the still-sleeping form under the pale blue linens. *Who are you, Cathy Donnelly,* he asked himself in puzzlement. *And how did you ever get involved with someone like me?*

The questions were frustrating, and the answers, when they came, would be more so, because no real blame could be placed on either of them. Their meeting and coming together was the result of unpredictable factors falling into place all at once. It was "after the fact" that had to be dealt with now.

Cathy lay sleeping on her stomach, her arms bent at the elbow so that slender, limp hands lay on either side of her head. Her lashes were dark and thick against her cheek, and she breathed evenly and gently through slightly parted lips. The sheet that had been used for cover had worked its way down almost to her waist, and the soft curved side of a breast, flattened under her own weight, was sensuously exposed. It suggested to Travis a mature ripeness that he well remembered and had enjoyed.

Travis watched her in curiosity for several long minutes until Cathy shifted positions with a deep sigh. Then he retreated, closing the door behind him. He remembered now deciding to pursue Cathy to Miami. It had been a compelling urge he didn't fully understand at the time. Yes, there had been the instinctive owning up to his responsibility for her condition once he'd figured that out, but it had also been much more than that. He wanted to know why she'd changed her mind about telling him she was pregnant. Then, too, something had been established between them beyond the pregnancy. He was sure of that. Some emotion and sense of connection, its exact nature continually eluding him. Nonetheless, the thought was strong and persistent that he couldn't leave her alone.

Travis also remembered clearly now how she'd gotten sick the night before. She'd looked like a little girl bent over the table, staring fixedly into her plate, her color changed quickly as she swayed with nausea. Holding her trembling body as she was forced to let go in so personal a way had torn viciously at his insides, stunning him, shaking him badly. He felt like a royal bastard. Not once had Cathy ranted and raved or accused him; she had simply accepted her circumstances with a stoic strength that had taken him by surprise and left him feeling totally inadequate. And then to have apologized to him! What did she have to be sorry for?

He had never considered the possibilities of any of his intimate relationships resulting in a pregnancy. For one thing, he was barely with any one woman for any length of time. Certainly not long enough to make such a commitment of such cataclysmic potential. His women companions were out to have a good time, with no responsibilities or ties. A pregnancy for any of them would have been inconvenient. For another thing, which only struck him now as he looked at his affairs in cold retrospect, none of his former lovers even approached being as innocent as Cathy.

In exactly the same way as it had hit Cathy, Travis began to realize how ludicrous and unfortunate it was that he knew next to nothing about this young woman who carried his seed, the fruits of one night's passion. He knew that physically she was pretty in an almost-adolescent way. Pure and sweet. Her eyes were almost hypnotic, they were so dark and rich, lost in the smallness of her face. She was little but by no means petite. She fit well against his length, Travis recalled pleasurably, and it had been easy to tilt his head just a little when he kissed her. And kissing her had proved that she wasn't the complete angel she appeared—just a novice. She knew how to respond to the searching of his mouth and that responsiveness had awakened in Travis a desire to know more and to believe that she was capable of giving more. When they'd both gotten past the shock of her virginity, she had shown a passion that was as surprising as it had been delightful. With a possessiveness that was entirely new to him, Travis was glad that he was first to be with her. And although he couldn't be absolutely positive, he would bet that he'd also so far been the last.

Travis also knew her to be rather romantic in her outlook on life. She demonstrated a sensitiveness to other people that made him suspect correctly that she would often put other people's considerations above her own. On the other hand, he guessed that with so strong a sense of fairness she would not allow herself to be taken for granted, either. Cathy was an idealist, a dreamer and believer. Travis wondered in self-derision if she'd lost any of those qualities since meeting him. Hurt almost invariably leads to disillusionment. And he recognized that she had been hurt.

Feeling helpless in his lack of knowledge, Travis wandered the apartment, noticing all the little personal things that made it uniquely Cathy's. There was a round glass vase brimming with a gathered bunch of dried baby's breath. A brass music box. A candy dish half filled with gumdrops. A Lucite paperweight with snowflakes floating permanently in place. A silk-screened graphic print that read, "Be of love (a little) more careful than of anything." Travis wondered with a frown what Cathy really knew of love. Was it any more than he knew, which was precious little in his own eyes.

Travis spotted a rather dog-eared first edition of *The Little Prince* next to her typewriter. He remembered Cathy saying it was her favorite book. Curious, he picked it up and leafed quickly through the slender volume, wondering what magic it held for her. But his eyes were caught by the white page still rolled into her typewriter and filled with neat lines and spaces. Travis read a word, a phrase, searched through whole sentences. And innocently, not considering the further invasion to Cathy, he began reading the nearly completed text of her essay.

It was in that reading that Travis learned of the belief she'd always held that she wouldn't have children. It was there he found out that she'd been raised essentially without benefit of maternal care. It was there he saw Cathy's confusion, doubts, fears and questions about being a mother and a woman. She had been painfully honest and open with feelings, and she obviously meant, through her writing, to share them with others.

Travis read it a second time—and a third. And it was then that the reality of Cathy as a whole person crystallized. She was not some vague personality that had passed briefly through his life with shattering results. She was someone with far more substance and hold on him than he'd imagined. Cathy's words impressed him as eloquent and thoughtful. Her ideas were well rounded and complete. Her prose moving and meaningful. Travis had never known anyone who could express so much feeling and make him believe it, too, through the mere use of words. Having experienced them, Travis now knew exacty who Cathy was.

She was hope. She was life and unfulfilled dreams and peace. Above all, she was the promise of a future returned to him anew.

Chapter Eight

Cathy came quietly from the bedroom, fully dressed in a slim denim skirt and a white blouse with short sleeves and a mandarin collar. She was shoeless, her feet silent on the smooth parquet floors. When she stepped slowly into the living-room entrance, she immediately spotted Travis half reclined on the love seat, reading her copy of *The Little Prince*. She'd expected that all of the previous night was a dream and that Travis hadn't really come to find her. But he was there.

His dark thick hair was attractively ruffled. He wore only jeans, and they sat so low on his hips that Cathy could see his navel and the thin dark line of hair starting below it and disappearing provocatively beneath his waistband. He held a cigarette between two fingers of a hand that also held the book as he read with deep concentration, furrowing his brow. The sudden raw-male sight of him created an unusual churning in Cathy, very different from the unpleasant one she'd had recently. This new feeling had a hint of excitement to it that moved through her in a warm swirl. Travis was, at that moment, the epitome of the heroic male, and that excited her, too. But Cathy didn't have any time to dwell on the sensation, as Travis finally looked up, noticing her presence.

Cathy hugged herself at the clarity and intent with which Travis stared back at her. The clear cat eyes seemed to miss nothing on her or about her. He might even have been smiling at her, but she couldn't be sure beneath the deep shadowing of his unshaved face. Cathy didn't understand what had happened since the night before, but Travis was not looking at her as a stranger or as a chance acquaintance would. There was knowledge in his gaze that exposed her to him all the more.

Travis's eyes swept quickly over her, and he raised a brow. "How are you feeling?" he asked in a deep, low voice.

Cathy found the tone caressing, and it made her blush as well as make her wonder at it. "I'm fine, thank you," she answered politely, and it definitely made Travis smile.

Travis uncurled his lean body from the sofa, and from under the thick veil of her lashes Cathy watched the sinewy length of him as he stood tall and masculine and half dressed. Travis put the cigarette out, dropped the book on the cushions and started toward her with a studied animal slowness and cadence. Cathy kept her eyes on the smooth plane of his chest, afraid that if their eyes met this close, the extraordinary feeling of attraction she felt would be clear to him. It was unexpected, and under the circumstances, Cathy thought breathlessly, somewhat out of place.

It nearly made her jump when Travis reached out a hand to slowly cup the side of her face, his palm along a jaw and his thumb lifting her chin. Curious, Cathy finally met his gaze. It was searching and filled with what could only be described as concern. That surprised her, too.

"You're still too pale," he observed with a frown. His thumb moved over her chin, touching her lips. Cathy let out a soft sigh of air, and Travis dropped his eyes to watch her mouth. "And much too thin," he said vaguely. But Cathy could feel her heart respond. It was not possible that he really cared. She knew that wasn't reasonable to expect, though she might want him to. Cathy lifted her chin away from his hand.

"I was always thin," she prevaricated. She glanced briefly at his face and bit her lip. "What—what about you? How do you feel?" she asked softly.

Travis raised a brow and a corner of his mouth. "You mean after the spectacle I made of myself last night?" he asked with caustic humor. "Not as bad as I look. I guess I'll survive."

She nodded. The silence between them was awkward. They were so unsure of themselves. Travis was not used to being concerned about someone other than himself. Not that he was incapable, just long out of practice—and that had been entirely by choice. And Cathy, though surrounded by men almost all of her life, had not enough knowledge to gauge Travis's reactions to her. This was so different from the time of their first meeting when there'd been nothing between them. Now they were lovers—and strangers.

"Look," Travis began again, grabbing her attention. "I'm sorry about last night. It probably didn't help that I yelled at you or went out and came back ripped or that I apparently collapsed on your bed—"

"That wasn't your fault," Cathy interrupted, trying to explain fairly. "I was the one who put you there."

Travis raised both brows. "Did you also undress me?"

A warm blush began creeping up Cathy's neck, and she moved around Travis's disturbingly half-dressed state and into the living room. "Yes. I couldn't very well let you sleep on the sofa. You wouldn't fit. And the floor is so hard..." Her voice trailed off at the slow, amused grin spreading over Travis's face.

"Did I, er, were you uncomfortable?" he asked in a caressing drawl.

"Not very," Cathy admitted quietly. "Well, except when I—I was sick earlier. I'm sorry that I—"

Travis came over and took hold of her upper arms, forcing Cathy to face him. His gaze was probing, his voice calm and understanding. "Cathy, that couldn't be helped. Let's not talk about it anymore. And let's stop apologizing." Slowly, Travis could feel her relax under his hands. He raked one of his hands through his hair and took a deep breath. "Right now I could really use some black coffee, and I think we could both do with something to eat. Why don't I make some breakfast?"

"I couldn't! I—I haven't been very hungry," Cathy answered, pressing her stomach and already imagining a distressing rumbling inside.

"You mean nothing stays down," Travis corrected with

insight as he watched her actions. "You can't go on not eating. You're pregnant, and you're going to need more nourishment!"

Cathy immediately straightened her spine and looked defensive at the presumptive tone of Travis's voice. She was suddenly recalling the authoritative posture of her father, brother and even Brian toward her for years, even though tempered with love, that had ruled her life. It had always been for the best, but now it was up to her to decide for herself what was best. "I don't eat breakfast," Cathy stated firmly.

"You will now," Travis countered, his tone equally even and firm. He started for the kitchen.

"Wait a minute!" Cathy called after him, totally indignant now. "*I'm* the one who's pregnant!"

Travis swung back to her, his eyes suddenly icy as they pierced hers. "And *I'm* the one responsible!"

Cathy was instantly silenced, and she swallowed any further retort that sat on her tongue. They faced each other for a horrible cold moment as the facts were placed between them. In that one instant they both experienced a brief wave of surprise and panic. It was true. There was the overwhelming fact of a pregnancy between them, and not much else. If Travis secretly thought to set things right in some way, Cathy was equally wishful that he could.

Cathy's chin came up, and her own dark eyes sparkled sharply. It somewhat surprised Travis further to see determination building within her. She *had* changed. She might appear innocent, and she was certainly not worldly, but if she had to, Cathy was perfectly capable of seeing herself through this alone. But that was not the point. Travis had no intention of leaving her alone to handle the situation. It was now his, as well.

"You have no rights over me, Travis. I can take care of myself," she said with quiet authority. Under his deeply tanned skin Travis flushed.

"I'm not here to exercise rights."

"Then why did you come?" Cathy asked curiously.

"Why did you come to tell me you were pregnant?" Travis shot back.

Cathy blinked. Why indeed. There had been so many reasons at the time. One had been hope that perhaps seeing him again would tell her what she was feeling and had been feeling about him since April. Had it been a spring fantasy, spring fever, a romantic infatuation that had overwhelmed her and brought them impossibly together? Was there the slightest chance that it was the beginning of something not quite so effervescent and tentative? "I—I don't know," Cathy confessed sadly. "I guess I thought that telling you was the right thing to do. I thought you should know."

"And then what?" Travis pursued.

Cathy bit down on her lip. "I don't know."

"Cathy, if you really believed that I should know, then why did you wait to tell me?" he asked, puzzled.

Her head came up sharply, and Cathy stared at him. Surely the reason was obvious. "I was concerned about your family. You had other responsibilities—to them."

Travis frowned at her. "That's the second time you've mentioned my family."

"One of us should!" Cathy suddenly said in exasperation. "You can't just pretend they don't exist!"

His eyes narrowed, his mouth tightening with private memories. "I've never done that."

"Well, you certainly don't belong here with me. There's Mrs. Hoyt and the kids—" And then Cathy stopped, fully expecting Travis to finally admit to it. But silence continued between them as her stomach knotted in apprehension with what Cathy knew had to be said.

Travis stared at her for a long time until, slowly, understanding set in. If he hadn't been so relieved, he might have laughed at her mistake. The thing that stopped him, however, was sudden further insight into her thinking. She had not actually been angry at the possibility of his being married but personally upset that if he was, then he was committed to and therefore in love with someone else. "Oh, Cathy!" Travis muttered in awareness, and he stepped forward slowly to put his arms around her.

Cathy was stiff for a second, but Travis did not give her a chance to pull away, closing his arms and bringing her against the warm firmness of his chest and thighs. He liked the feel of her against him. He remembered it. She fit well, her curly hair brushing his chin. Travis brought his head down a bit so that his chin and jaw now rubbed in her hair.

"Cathy...Melinda Hoyt is not my wife. She's my sister-in-law. The two kids are my nephews, Jonathan and Matthew."

Cathy was still for a moment, and Travis wondered if she'd heard him. But in his position he couldn't see the mist of tears that blurred her vision at his words. Nor could he see how welcome they were, almost making her knees weak. Tentatively, Cathy raised her hands and rested them on his bare chest. Travis fingered her curls.

"Obviously, Melinda neglected to tell you that," he said ruefully.

Cathy nodded, her head moving slowly against his skin. "Yes, she did."

Travis understood more clearly now what the past week must have been like for her. He wished fervently now that he'd been at the houseboat when she'd arrived. Travis ran his hand up and down her back, felt her breath sweet and warm on his chest. "I'm not married, Cathy." Travis paused for an obvious moment. "But I—I used to be." He could feel her immediate reaction, and automatically Travis tightened his arms. "It was for a very brief time a very long time ago. Do you understand?" he asked. Travis made it clear this was the beginning and the end of all he was going to say about it. It was no longer important.

"Yes," Cathy mumbled.

"I've done some lousy things in my life, but I'm not that much of a bastard!" Travis added caustically. Cathy lifted her face and looked at him for a long, poignant moment. A dozen different emotions expressed themselves in her face, and Travis carefully watched each one. Her eyes were bright with an appeal that she was unaware of and to which Travis was uncertain as to how to respond. There was a weariness and fatigue and confusion. He absently reached to touch her cheek with the tips of several long fingers.

"The baby is mine, and I know it," Travis began again. Cathy flushed deeply and dropped her eyes. "Neither of us expected this, but now that it's happened, we should deal with it together. I won't leave you alone. We'll talk about it and think about it carefully. But we'll do it together."

Cathy felt a surge of joy at his words, even as she still felt the need to make it easy for him, release him of any responsibility for her. She looked squarely at him. "You really don't have to stay. I'd understand if—"

"No, you wouldn't," Travis contradicted, scowling dangerously at her.

Cathy started to speak again, but the phone rang, startling them. It rang a second time before either moved. Then Travis pushed her gently away.

"Go on and answer it. I'll make some coffee." He turned to the kitchen.

Cathy gave no real thought as to who might be on the phone, so when she answered and heard her brother's voice, it took several seconds for her to orient herself and reply. Then mumbling a hello and acutely aware of Travis in the next room, Cathy realized guiltily that it had been more than two weeks since she'd spoken to Chad.

"Hey Cat. How's it going?"

"H-hello, Chad. How are you?" Cathy asked nervously, taking furtive looks over her shoulder in the direction of the kitchen while also trying to keep her voice low.

"I was worried. I expected to hear from you last week. Is everything all right?"

"Yes, of course. Why—why shouldn't it be?"

"You tell me! I suppose you're still getting settled. Anything new going on in Florida?"

Cathy closed her eyes helplessly against the unavoidable significance of the question and the answer. "Not—not much," she responded breathlessly, her stomach tensing with the lie.

"Are you sure you're okay?" Chad questioned. "You sound funny."

Cathy attempted a light laugh. It bordered on hysteria. "Chad, I'm okay. Really! It's just that I've been busy with my apartment—and I'm writing a lot. Wasn't that the whole idea?''

''If you say so,'' he said, chuckling.

Cathy sighed. ''I know you think this—this urge of mine is silly, but—''

''Not silly. Just unnecessary. You could do all the writing you want right here in Baltimore. And you would have been near Brian. I think he misses you.''

''Does he?'' Cathy asked with a curious lack of interest, her guilt doubling nonetheless.

''You mean he hasn't called you to tell you so?'' Chad chuckled again.

No, he hadn't, but Cathy chose not to say so. She realized that she hadn't missed the calls. Brian had never been a demonstrative person except when talking politics. Their personal relationship, so long established and understood, was also just taken for granted. And although he had disapproved of her need for some time spent alone and by herself, it probably never occurred to him to call her once in a while to say hello or that he missed her. Maybe he really didn't. Brian did not have the charisma of Travis, nor had he ever affected Cathy the way Travis did. Brian began to pale significantly in comparison, and she began to feel worse. In any case, Cathy wasn't forced to respond, as Chad was off again on another subject.

''So how does it feel being out of Baltimore and on your own? Is it what you thought it would be?''

''I'm still finding out,'' Cathy said with a sigh. ''But I'm glad I decided to get away. I needed to get away.''

''I know how you feel, Cathy. And I understand even if I do tease you,'' Chad said seriously. ''But you've never been so far from home or family before. I don't want anything to happen to you.''

Cathy squeezed her eyes closed and sat down on the edge of the sofa. If only he knew. Would Chad be shocked, angry, hurt, appalled? Would his understanding stretch as far as dealing with his sister's being pregnant by a man she'd never mentioned before and knew so little about? Something *had* already happened to her. She didn't understand it all yet. She had no hope, therefore, of justifying it to her brother. Suddenly, Cathy felt very sad and hurt, and for a long moment she let the self-pity melt through her before forcing a deep breath of air inside to calm herself.

"I can take care of myself," she told Chad, repeating the very same words she'd said minutes ago to Travis, as if also trying to convince herself of it. But could she really?

"Yeah, well...just remember you can always come home," her brother reminded her affectionately.

On her end Cathy gave a wan smile, her chin quivering. "I'll remember," she said lightly.

"Good! Well, I have to go. I'm supposed to shoot a reception this afternoon in Washington, and I need to pick up some filters first. You take care."

"I will. And Chad?"

"Yeah?"

"Thanks for calling," Cathy said warmly.

Chad laughed softly. "Anytime...No. As a matter of fact, next time it's your turn to call!"

Cathy joined in the laughter. "I promise I will. 'Bye."

Cathy hung up the phone, and her smile slowly faded. She sat rather dejected and pensive until a glass of orange juice was suddenly passed in front of her and pressed into a limp hand. She looked up quickly, blinking away tears, and found Travis standing over her, his eyes dark and intent on her. He'd put on a shirt and combed his hair and shaved. Cathy stared at him for a second, adjusting to the difference in his appearance.

"Drink it," Travis ordered her quietly, nodding to her glass.

Cathy took a few sips, and Travis lowered himself to the space next to her on the love seat. Her conversation with Chad fresh in her mind kept Cathy silent, and she didn't volunteer whom she'd spoken to. And although he was more than just curious, Travis didn't ask. Instead, he brought the conversation back to where it had been interrupted with his next question to her.

"Have you told anyone about the baby?" he asked.

"No, I haven't." Cathy bit her lip. "Only Elizabeth Harris knows."

"Elizabeth Harris?" Travis questioned.

"She's with a women's health center. It was Elizabeth who told me I—I was pregnant."

"You didn't suspect before that?"

"I had no idea," Cathy murmured with a kind of bewildered openness. And when Travis remembered what he'd read in her essay, he realized that there were many things she didn't know, and which confused her. And she had come to him a virgin. His jaw tensed, and he nodded.

"I see..." Keeping his eyes on her for reaction, Travis then asked quietly, "And what about an abortion? You hinted you would have one."

Cathy looked quickly at him, her great dark eyes soft liquid pools that shimmered now with emotion. She found herself hesitating to tell him she hadn't meant it. "Maybe," Cathy said in a vague voice.

Travis stared hard at her for a long time, a hand clenching tightly and then relaxing. "Then you don't want to have the baby?" he asked stiffly.

With a sort of moan, Cathy quickly put down the glass of juice and stood up, wrapping her arms around her body. She took several steps away from Travis, her back to him. "I'm not sure what I'm doing," Cathy murmured to herself, shaking her head until the curls feathered down in front of her eyes. Not want the baby—Cathy couldn't speak because she didn't know how to answer. She was so confused. Should she tell him she could want *his* baby? She heard Travis move to stand close behind her. Every nerve in her body went stiff and tight, and she almost couldn't breathe.

"Then don't do it," Travis said in a tight, hard voice. "If you're not sure, don't do anything!"

Cathy then glanced over her shoulder at him, having finally registered something in his voice and tone, something in the way he stood so alertly near her. Cathy could now feel his own tension. She was puzzled. "Don't—don't you want me to—to have one, too?"

Travis immediately made to speak and then changed his

mind. Cathy watched him take a deep breath and expel it, choosing his words carefully as he started again. "I just don't want you to do anything you're not sure of and that you may regret later. Wait a while."

She found herself wanting to be honest with him. She didn't know what Travis hoped to accomplish by being there, but Elizabeth Harris had been right—the decision had to be hers. But she found herself wondering what Travis would want her to do.

Cathy's eyes clouded. She'd thought maybe there was something else. But Travis said no more, and she could read nothing in his closed expression. Cathy sighed and turned her back again. "It's not going to be easy—" And then she stopped. She was going to say how little she knew about being a mother and raising a child. But she didn't want to influence Travis's response.

Travis continued to pursue his original question. "And I suppose that an abortion is easier?" he asked, misunderstanding her comment. "Will it solve everything?"

Cathy gasped suddenly, staring wide-eyed at him. "Travis, you don't understand! It's not easier. It's horrid to think anyone *likes* having an abortion! It's a terrible decision to have to make."

Travis turned impatiently away from her for a second, and Cathy watched with a frown. Travis knew about making hard choices. The ones that hurt his family and kept him separated from them for so many years. Ones that he consciously made for himself but that were lonely and sad. He came back to her, his eyes nearly gray as they blazed brightly in frustration.

"The decision is mine," Cathy reminded him now in a clear, steady voice. "I have to decide what to do . . . what is best." She would still not hand over any responsibility to him.

"But you're not sure?" Travis also reminded her.

Cathy's look didn't waver this time, but she said no more.

Travis swept his hands through his hair. "You do have other choices," he informed her.

"Such as?"

Travis stood still, looking at her before coming closer and allowing his eyes to soften as they searched her up-turned face. "You could marry me," he said.

For a moment Cathy wasn't sure she'd actually heard him say it. Instantly, she knew she wanted to say yes. She wished she could, but that would have been a grave dis-service to them both. Cathy believed in love and affec-tion, respect, care and tenderness. She believed in a marriage that was based on these and not on mere conve-niences. His eyes looked so warm and reassuring. If only there was more to go on. What did Travis think of her? About her being pregnant? Did he blame her? How did he really feel? Cathy lifted her chin. Whatever it was, she wouldn't have him feel sorry for her or ashamed. And she didn't need his guilt. She had plenty of her own. There wasn't enough, then, to make her say yes.

"No, Travis, I can't. It wouldn't be fair."

Travis tensed his jaw stubbornly. "And I can't let you do the other. *That* wouldn't be fair. I'm staying here until we find the right thing to—"

"The right thing!" Cathy twisted away impatiently. "Maybe there is no such thing as right!" She sighed tired-ly, rubbing at her temple. "Oh, Travis... There's nothing you can do here. There's no reason to stay."

"And what if I say I want to stay with you," he per-sisted angrily.

Cathy was about to continue her objections when another thought occurred to her. "Here... with me?" she voiced naively.

Travis let out a deep breath and shrugged his shoulders lightly. "Why not?" Then Cathy's eyes stretched wide, and Travis correctly interpreted her thinking. "There's very little we don't know about each other, Cathy. We needn't be uncomfortable. I think we can both share the bed. As you pointed out, the floor is too hard and the sofa is too small," he said with raised brows and some humor, but Cathy continued to stare at him as if assessing him.

Actually, Cathy was assessing herself. Her heart lurched and changed beats in her chest, Travis's nearness imprint-ing itself on all her senses. It frightened her to recognize that she was no longer ignorant of a man's desires or needs, but even more than that, that she had been awakened to her own. She'd not forgotten the closeness beyond the ultimate physical intimacy that was there between them for a few hours that night in April. Even now as she fought with a serious decision affecting them both and with which he could take no part, Cathy wanted to lose herself in his embrace, relearn the overwhelming masculine power of him and share the ecstasy that he alone had taught her.

It was crazy to want him this way, to need him. How much more complicated could her life and his get if he stayed?

Travis watched the wavering considerations and the indecision brighten her eyes with hope and flush her cheeks with confusion. "After all, we didn't do so badly last night," he added.

Cathy focused her attention on him and his remark. She shook her head at him. "No, but you were drunk last night. I was safe enough."

Travis chose not to tell her she'd also spent most of the night asleep in his arms. "I'll stay sober, and you'll still be safe. I won't make love to you if that's what you're afraid of. I promise—that is, unless you change your mind."

"Your promises have a habit of backfiring!" Cathy said tartly, ignoring his added comment even though the idea made her blush. Travis tightened his mouth and quirked a corner of it in a bleak imitation of a smile.

"Sometimes... But I won't get in the way. I have reconnaissance to fly for the weather service here in Miami. You can write. Somehow in between we'll work on what we should do. We have to try."

Cathy was suddenly deeply moved by his persistence and felt her throat constrict with feeling. "It could take a long time," she said hoarsely.

"There's enough time to be sure," Travis responded, taking hold of her shoulders in his large hands, misunderstanding her concern. "We can still be married," he said in a low, deep voice, oddly hopeful.

Cathy closed her eyes, biting on her bottom lip and

shaking her head again. That was too much of a sacrifice, especially if he didn't love her. Travis squeezed her shoulders, giving her a little shake. "It can work! Or I'll help you if—if you just want to keep the baby. I'll stay to see you through it."

Cathy wanted to ask suddenly what happens afterward, but didn't. Right now was enough to work out. She searched deeply into his cool gray-green eyes, searched deeply within herself. "Is it...really so important to stay?" Then she practically held her breath waiting for his response.

Travis could see the expectancy in her eyes, the curious hesitancy. He'd asked himself that same question. There were a half-dozen responses he could have given to allay her fears. In the end he gave her the only one that truly mattered. "What happens to you is important to me," he said simply, his deep voice low and caressing.

A relief such as Cathy wouldn't have believed possible swept through her. She had been so tense that her now-relaxing body started to tremble and made way for another emotion to seep in and attack her already-weakened defenses.

"Cathy..." Travis said her name, seeing the panic at last grab her. Slowly, he came forward to pull her into his arms. "Don't be afraid." He soothed her with infinite tenderness, pressing her shaking body against him. Cathy was breathing heavily as she fought losing control entirely. She held on to Travis, accepting the support and strength he offered. "Shh," he whispered against her forehead. "Everything will work out."

Travis pulled his head back just enough to look down at her and with a free hand under her chin lifted her face so he could see her expression. Her eyes were swimming in tears, and when one rolled down her smooth cheek to the corner of her quivering mouth, it was Travis's undoing. "Don't cry," he whispered, and slowly he bent and pressed his firm cool lips lightly to hers. He did it again. Travis repeated this several times, administering feathery kisses, his mouth plying and pulling gently. His comforting changed her breathing, forcing her concentration elsewhere. He heard a low sob of protest, but he ignored it, continuing to tease until her mouth pursed and responded lightly, too. The crying stopped, and the tears were salty in his mouth. Cathy's breathing finally became soft and sighing, and she leaned into him.

Travis pulled the anguish from her, took charge of it, giving her a measure of peace, surprising even himself. He waited until her lips gently parted, and even more gently he began to kiss her with more intent, his tongue discovering the slight opening and moistening her lips. Travis had meant to comfort her, to assure her that he had no intention of deserting her. She had been needy of that comforting—and so had he.

Putting a hand into her curls to tilt her head, Travis manipulated her mouth open farther so that he could kiss her with the depth and feeling that had suddenly taken over. He now found her equally responsive, her breathing gently hurried, her mouth soft, allowing him complete access to the dark, sweet center. Recognition rekindled in both of them. It stripped away the exterior of uncertainty and lapsed time. It stripped away fear and reestablished feelings and desires and made them real. The tension that had kept them strangers dissolved.

Cathy pressed against his chest, flattening her breasts but feeling secure there. Travis held her waist, pulled her to his stomach, flat and hard and strong. She felt his thighs—taut and bold—and understood a basic need. She quivered. He tightened his arms. Travis's tongue made repeated delightful forays, exploring her mouth until Cathy felt dazed and a stirring in her loins that instantly brought to mind Travis's initiating her to desire and pleasure. But she couldn't allow herself that. Not now.

Cathy put her hands to his chest and pushed away. Reluctantly, Travis released her mouth but kept her within the circle of his arms. Slowly, Cathy raised her eyes, past the firm square chin and the full wide mouth. Past the faintly flaring nostrils, all the way to his sea-hued eyes, dark and nearly emerald—intense.

Travis easily read her reaction to him and also the questioning thoughts behind her dark, searching sable eyes.

He raised a brow at her, amusement in the smile he gave her. "I said I wouldn't jump all over you—unless you wanted me to. But I never promised not to kiss you, Cat."

Cathy gave a shy glance and smile to him, blushing. Her pretty mouth had been made lovelier by his kisses. But Cathy smiled, because his words were practically an admission that he might kiss her again. And because his use of a nickname had been said with such affection. That was a start.

"Cathy?" Travis reached to kiss just her forehead. A hand slid up her back, holding her close. "Will you call Elizabeth? Will you tell her you haven't decided yet?"

There was a long silence around them, between them, before Travis felt her head nod slightly.

"All right," she said softly. Cathy started to speak to tell him the decision she'd made to keep the baby, but Travis laid a finger across her lips, not wanting her to change her mind or to think about it anymore for the present.

"Before we do any more talking, we eat! Breakfast?" he asked. And in support his stomach suddenly added strong growling pleas of its own. Cathy gave a short giggle and smiled up to him, tears still sitting on her lashes.

"Okay...breakfast!"

Chapter Nine

"Hello. May I talk with Ms Catherine Donnelly, please?"

"Yes, speaking."

"Hi, Catherine. This is Valerie Banner at *Miami Magazine*."

Cathy came instantly alert, her heart skipping one excited beat. "Y-yes?" she mouthed as she sat up straight and turned off her typewriter.

"I got the piece you sent me last week. I've read it and shown it to another editor here. We like it very much."

"I—I'm very pleased," Cathy got out, almost holding the air in so she wouldn't sound so breathless.

"We've decided to purchase it for publication. I very much like what you've written about the transitions between childhood and being an adult, and the traditional assumption that being over twenty-one automatically makes one an adult. In a town that is predominantly older citizens, I think you managed a refreshing look at maturing and being young."

"Thank you!" Cathy said humbly, enjoying the praise nonetheless.

"I'm not sure when it will run yet. Maybe we can fit it into the October format. Would that be okay with you?"

Cathy opened her mouth and closed it again, swallowing. She was being asked what she wanted. Someone was taking her seriously, treating her professionally and telling her she had something important to say and contribute to others. "I—I have no objections to that. October sounds fine."

"Good! I'll try to get a check in the mail to you before

the end of the week. Have you done much of this first-person-observation sort of writing?"

"No, not much," Cathy admitted. "Mostly just a lot of poetry. As a matter of fact, I'm working on a book of verse right now."

Valerie laughed softly. "Oh, you want to be a literary writer—serious, heavy-duty stuff!"

"Well..." Cathy hesitated, wondering why Valerie thought it amusing.

"Oh, don't get me wrong. I think if you can do it you should. Especially if you've always wanted to. But my guess is you also have a talent for commentaries and essays. What else have you written?"

Cathy wound the cord of the phone around her fingers and fiddled nervously with it. "I—I just finished a piece on motherhood and what it means to different women. It's coming out in a newsletter at the Women's Alternative Health Center."

"Umm... That's interesting. How do you feel about motherhood? Are you a mother, by the way?"

Cathy gnawed on her lip. "N-No, I'm not. Not yet," she added innocently, the implications bypassing her. "I'm confused on the issue. Quite honestly, I'm still trying to decide if I know enough about myself to be a good mother."

There was a long silence on the line. Cathy frowned, wondering what had happened. Then Valerie finally spoke again.

"You know, listening to you has given me an idea. I wonder if they'd let me do a series of articles on women. Would you be interested in writing some more stuff on the subject? Would it interfere with the book you're working on?"

"No, not at all! And I'd love to write more for you. That is, if you really think it's good."

"Oh, your writing's good; there's no question about that. But look, I'm jumping way ahead of myself. Tell you what. Why don't we meet for lunch and talk about it."

"I'd like that."

"Fine. Now let me just dig out my appointment calendar."

When Cathy got off the phone, she was so stunned she sat staring at the receiver in her hand in total disbelief. She had sold her second article in less than two weeks, the first one being to Elizabeth Harris. Coming to her senses, Cathy put down the receiver and, closing her eyes, let out a breath of joy and anticipation. It was one thing to claim to be a writer; it was another thing to have others agree that she was one. Cathy wanted to let everyone know that she was. She wanted to tell her brother Chad. She wanted to tell Travis first of all. Brian never crossed her mind.

She tried to imagine Travis's reaction when he heard the news. That is, if she had a chance to tell him. She hadn't seen or heard from him since the morning before. Would he be happy for her? Would he care at all? Or would he continue in the erratic way he had been behaving for the few weeks since he'd literally moved in with her? Sometimes he'd show gentle concern and affection, sometimes impatience. She didn't always understand him, or even what it was he wanted or expected from her. But no matter what his reaction was going to be, she wanted to celebrate, and she wanted him to be part of it. Oddly enough, Travis was partly responsible for her writing getting done at all.

Cathy had found it harder to discipline herself than she had anticipated. It was far too easy to write for just a while and then spend the rest of the time indulging in daydreams or just reading. Moreover, she often found herself so tired in the afternoons that a short nap was becoming part of her routine. But Travis had been firm with her, telling her bluntly she was never going to be a writer unless she sat down and actually did the work. He himself put her on a schedule of working for three hours in the morning, taking a break and doing three more in the afternoon. At first she resented his dictatorial attitude, although pleased that he took that much interest. Of course, when she'd sent in the essay to Elizabeth Harris and had it accepted, they'd both been so pleased that Travis had swept her happily in his arms, hugging her and giving her a brief but nonetheless bone-shattering, thorough kiss. It had been spontaneous, but it left them momentarily silent and aware. After that, Cathy began to feel settled when he was with her, lonely and pensive when he was away on assignment.

It was a strange relationship they had—and contradictory. Cathy had adjusted rather quickly to his being in the apartment, probably due, to a large extent, to her having grown up in a house of men. But Travis was not just any man. He was someone who she'd been as intimate with as it was humanly possible to be. He was someone who sparked a sensual awareness deep within her with his very presence and in whom her interest couldn't be denied. But outwardly Cathy treated him diffidently—politely and accommodatingly but remotely—as if keeping him at arm's length would dispel the other feelings she was developing with each passing day and keep her safe.

Travis was presumptuous with her at times, watching her sternly and giving her orders as if she hadn't the least idea how to take care of herself now that she was pregnant, as if he were an expert. He sometimes treated her like a wayward child, which exasperated her and often led to arguments. He made her eat regularly, and watched what she did with a careful, protective air of a parent. Or at the very least, as if he were preparing. But Cathy never detected that. And she didn't want him to treat her that way. In all honesty, neither did Travis. But it was safer. Cathy had never been sure what good his presence would do. But she recognized a gladness that he was there and thought better of their possibilities together than his just acting as baby-sitter.

For his part, Travis at first spent a great deal of his time being acutely aware of her developing femininity, her slender curved prettiness and softness, accompanied by a maturing of her personality and character. He was also taken by her energy and imagination, by her cockeyed observations. Yet, as naive and fantastic as he sometimes found them, her ideas had the ability to make him think, as they also made him impatient. He sometimes wanted to shout at her to grow up.

"One of the things I've learned in life," he reminded

her, "is not to walk around with my head in the clouds, Cathy. You end up getting hurt that way." *Or hurting people yourself,* Travis thought bitterly. But Cathy had only shaken her head sadly at him as if he didn't understand or had a lot to learn.

"Oh, Travis. You sound just like Brian," Cathy had said unwittingly. Travis stiffened in his chair, his hands clenching. He didn't have to ask who Brian was. He could feel it in the way the name hung in the air like a curse for uncomfortable moments between them. "You both suffer from tunnel vision. You spend so much time expecting the worst that can happen that you miss the wonderful things going on around you."

Travis swept his hand through his hair and sighed. "You don't know what you're talking about!" he muttered. "You sound just like that book you're so fond of—*The Little Prince*!" He made a dismissing gesture. "How the hell can you see anything past all that—that stardust in your eyes?"

"So instead you bury your head in the sand! What's the difference between my dreaming and your running away?"

"Just what is it I'm supposed to be running from?" he asked with a raised caustic brow.

Cathy looked at him for a long moment, remembering and knowing more than he thought she did. "Whatever happened in the past that lives on in your dreams at night."

He had no response at all to her observation, neither confirming nor denying it.

Cathy kept her promise to contact Elizabeth, although only to let her know that Travis had found her.

Travis, believing that she was still contemplating an abortion, was not ignorant of the fact that she was playing a chancy game with time and had to come to a decision soon. And he knew that the decision had to be her own. He hoped that in some way she would see that her decision was equally important to him, but he didn't blame her that she didn't. Travis could never say how much her decision meant, because he himself did not know. He had not a clue as to how he was really going to be of help to her. It was really that he just needed to be with her. They were irrevocably tied to each other, and he had to stay, hoping to make their connection real and permanent.

He would have married her at once if she'd agreed, not holding marriage in the same romantic reverence as Cathy did, which was for her serious and sacred. Perhaps his past disastrous marriage precluded that. But he did see marriage as a means that would legally bind her to him and as an influence on her decision about the baby. Cathy never referred to the baby as such and was actually much more concerned with what she would do afterward. The future continued to be a source of great confusion and tension within her. The state of being pregnant she accepted for the moment as something happening to her body. But she blocked out the process and changes that would take place over the next seven or eight months.

However, Travis found that Cathy didn't seem to have any shame or embarrassment where her body was concerned. It wasn't exactly a lack of modesty, but he would guess that her thinking was now that there was indeed nothing to hide. He kept his promise not to make love to her in the double bed they shared, which was getting smaller every night. He insisted, first of all, that Cathy go to bed first. Travis would then sit in the living room, for hours if need be, smoking until he was sure she'd fallen to sleep. Then he would quietly undress and slip into bed next to her. It was too disconcerting to catch glimpses of her moving half-dressed from the bath to the bedroom and downright tantalizing to watch her peel off everything as she readied for bed. Her short yellow nightgown was a minor insignificant detail between them.

For long moments Travis would lie in bed enjoying the warmth and sweetness her body had spread throughout the linens and the curled up softness of her limbs. With the best of intentions Travis would sleep stiffly on the edge of his space, only to wake each day to find his arms closed securely around her, her head on his shoulder or her back snuggled into his chest, spoon fashion. Each day he'd force himself out of bed first to shower and dress and leave, if he had to, instead of obeying the deeper, growing urge within to let her awaken drowsily in his embrace and let whatever happened happen.

To some extent the arrangement made Cathy trust him completely, without reservation. For a week or more he'd slept in the same bed with her without overt sexual advances. Cathy was sadly convinced that he wasn't attracted to her at all. If Travis had any idea as to what she was thinking, he would have set about immediately to prove her wrong—promise or no promise. Each day in her presence made him more and more ready to claim her again as his own and show her the full extent of his feelings.

Cathy was sometimes sure that as she turned in the night, it was against Travis, with his arms encouraging her closer. She eagerly complied, finding the haven comforting, strong and with a dawning sense of inevitability, which was gone by morning, that this was where she belonged. But Travis's quick early departures often squelched the dream. Cathy wavered constantly between the feeling that he might really care for her, and that he was only feeling responsible and guilty for her being pregnant.

Cathy's being pregnant was never actually spoken of. But both understood that it was happening and responded to it differently. For Cathy it remained a source of marvel, fear, joy and dread, her confusion not abating with the time they spent together or the evidence that her body was already changing subtly. For Travis it was a reminder that he'd stripped her of the last of her innocence and hurt her deeply by leaving her so vulnerable and unprepared. And as much as Cathy worried about her abilities as a mother, Travis wondered what kind of father he'd make. His own father had tossed out to him the repeated prophecy that when he, Travis, was a father, he'd know how hard it was to be one. Of course, that proclamation when he was a teenager had been taken in the same light as all the others—an attempt through dire parental threats to make him straighten up and see the error of his ways. And it was true that at eighteen he had no appreciation of what it was like to be a father. But that did not mean he didn't eventually want to be one. Cathy's seeming decision, then, to have an abortion had sent shock waves ricocheting through him. Finally, the magnitude of their individual positions, of their individual responsibility and concerns, their needs and wants, became clear.

Travis still half expected Cathy to turn on him with accusations and rage and to declare that she would get an abortion and be done with it. But she never did, until her very trust and hopefulness made him feel even worse. And one night, after they'd finished a dinner that she'd cooked, he'd stood in the kitchen doorway as she put food away and questioned her on it.

"Aren't you ever angry at me?" he asked, his jaw tensing as he waited for her answer.

"Only when you make me drink milk and not let me have coffee or wine!" Cathy absently teased as she worked.

"For heaven's sake!" Travis bit out through clenched teeth. He swept a hand through his thick hair at her flip response.

"Why should I be angry?" Cathy asked, trying to be serious for his sake.

"For doing this to you."

Cathy looked at him as the color rose pink in her face with understanding. She turned back to the sink, missing the anxiety and need for forgiveness showing in Travis's rugged face. She shrugged lightly. "You haven't done anything to me."

"And what about the baby? What about the fact that you're pregnant?"

Cathy turned now to look squarely at him. Her chin lifted defiantly, but her eyes were soft and a rich warm chocolate. "You didn't do this to me, Travis. This is something we did together."

Travis had stared at her, seeing the strength in her carriage and in her words. "Then marry me," he whispered hoarsely, keeping his eyes on her face, "so we can be responsible together." Cathy's own eyes searched his intently. There was a sparkling brightness in her look, like hope. But Travis saw it die and saw the tears unexpectedly welling up, her chin quivering.

"No," Cathy said tightly, leaving no room for compromise. "No...no...no!" she repeated, her voice rising higher with each utterance as she turned from him, brushing past to flee to her room. Travis started to follow after her but thought better of it, leaving her alone.

She came out eventually, solemn and quiet with evidence that she'd been crying. But she merely sat at her desk, leafing through finished work and scribbling new notes. The silence between them had been thick and deadly, and Travis, not content to let the subject drop, came to stand over her, glaring at her in frustration.

"Why won't you marry me, dammit?" His vehemence stunned her. Cathy sighed wearily.

"Because I don't want you doing me any favors just because of the baby. And because you don't love me."

"I'm trying to help!" Travis said impatiently.

"Then do me a favor," Cathy said, the strain on both their nerves making her sound more angry than she was. "*Don't* be so kind! In a year we'd hate each other. In two years we'd be divorced. When I marry, it will be for the right reasons!"

"And isn't this reason enough? You pregnant with my child?"

Cathy shook her head. "Lots of people raise kids alone. My father did."

"Your father started out a little more advantaged than you."

Cathy raised her chin, and her eyes flashed stubbornly. "I can raise this baby alone if—if I have to," she said with bravado, her voice nonetheless breaking.

Travis stood still and stared at her. "Are you saying you'll have the baby?" he asked softly.

Cathy swallowed, and her shoulders slumped in near defeat. She raised tear-filled eyes to him, defiant, defensive...and confused. "I—I don't know," she finally answered, leaving them right back where they'd started.

Travis had muttered an expletive under his breath and, grabbing his jacket, had left the apartment abruptly without another word. Perhaps they both needed some time alone. But the time did little for Cathy and only made her cry all over again. And it only left them both tense, needy of comfort and afraid to ask for it. And when it was given, the spontaneity of it made it more worthwhile.

There was the night, for example, when she'd awakened to several sharp cramping pains in her abdomen that had pulled her instantly awake, clutching her middle. The pains had seemed severe, but Cathy couldn't be sure, now that she was awake. She simply lay for some time feeling uncomfortable and achy in her stomach. It had happened before but had always gone quickly away. Quietly, she got out of bed, and holding a hand pressed to her stomach, went to the bathroom. She was warm and sticky with sweat both from the late June temperatures and humidity and the wrenching pain. Cathy washed her face in cold water, holding the cloth to her burning cheeks until she felt better. But she didn't really. For a moment she thought she was going to be sick, but the nausea passed, too. Then there came a knock on the bathroom door.

"Cat?"

"Y-yes?" she whispered weakly, stopping all her movements.

"Are you all right?" Travis asked in his deep voice.

"Yes...yes, I'm fine." There was a long pause.

"Are you sure?" he persisted, his voice suspicious and hard.

Chewing her lip in lingering discomfort, Cathy turned off the water, took a deep breath and opened the door. She again put a hand to her stomach. Travis was a tall shadow in front of her, naked the way she knew he slept, his own unique body heat emitting from him. She tried to keep her voice light and unconcerned, but it sounded thin and shaky even to her own ears.

"Yes. I—I just had some cramps. That's all."

Trvis reached a hand to the side of her face, and it felt so cool and soothing on her hot skin. She instinctively rubbed her cheek against his touch. Travis took his other hand and pressed it gently to her stomach, pushing her own hand away. Cathy looked inquiringly up at him, barely making out the straight line of his mouth, the ominous brows hiding his questioning, alert eyes.

"Does it still hurt?"

Cathy found herself smiling at his reference, enormously moved by the sound of worry in his voice. She shook her head. "No. It's all gone now."

But Travis continued to hold her as Cathy allowed the lethargy of his concern to melt over her, loving it and indeed feeling the pain go away.

"Maybe you should see the doctor tomorrow." His hand moved over the nylon-covered area of her stomach, sending a delightful shiver through her with the possessive movement.

"Don't be silly. I'm okay...really!"

Still he watched her. Then he let out a breath and ran his hand over the softness of her curls to the back of her head. The hand then pulled her gently toward him. They never actually touched except for Travis's hand on her stomach and the back of her head. But Cathy could feel the heat of him and sensed the firmness of his long body. For a second she swayed forward, wanting to place her cheek on his chest, wanting to curl her arms around him and hold tightly. The slow movement of his hand on her stomach made her smile in the dark as she again tilted her face up to him.

"I'm not a crocodile, you know," she quoted in an amused soft drawl. There was a long silence before the significance became clear to Travis. Then he gave her a lopsided grin at the private meaning. It curved his full mouth slightly, but his eyes, darkened out of sight, remained skeptical.

"Come on. Get back to bed," he ordered in a husky voice. And Cathy walked contentedly past him.

Other than the effect that her close physical proximity had on his mental, emotional and physical state, Travis slept well enough, unhampered by his dreams. There was, in fact, only one night in which the terror began to possess him. But Cathy, alert to his twisting and turning in the space next to her, merely reached out a hand to stroke his jaw and rough cheek soothingly.

"Travis..." She called his name once in a sleepy murmur. He grunted softly, rolling his head in her direction, and slept again without further incident.

And then the next morning, the last time she'd seen him, he was making breakfast, a habit and chore that became uniquely his. Travis seemed efficient and comfortable in a kitchen, like someone used to being alone. Cathy again approached him on the subject of his dreams. He was barefoot and dressed in only jeans, another habit that seemed to be his wont, his face as yet unshaved and his hair combed with his fingers. He was quiet that morning. No questions about how she felt or whether she had taken the pills Elizabeth had suggested. He had his own private concerns, and she knew beyond a doubt what they were.

"Travis?"

"Yeah?" he answered absently, cracking two eggs into a bowl.

"Tell me who Mitch is."

His hands stopped for a bare instant as he reached for salt and pepper, and Cathy waited to hear his reply. He wasn't evasive this time, however. Continuing his preparations, his back to her, Travis answered. "He was my brother. He's dead now," he replied sotto voce. A fork was whisked briskly through the mixture and another egg added. Cathy silently absorbed the information.

"Was he Melinda's husband?"

"Yes..." came the short response. He didn't want to talk about it, but Cathy wasn't discouraged by his lack of enthusiasm.

Cathy simply knew now that it was a subject that he obviously needed to talk about, and she thought she knew why. Thinking about how to begin, she laid the table for the two of them, falling into the routine they'd adopted quickly and easily as if it were the most natural thing in the world. In her mind she pieced together the bits of information she already had. Travis moaning Mitch's name in anguish. The burn scars on his arms and hands. The references to heat and explosions.

Travis divided the scrambled eggs between two plates, adding buttered toast and fresh orange wedges.

"How did he die?" Cathy asked into the tense air of the

room, her heart beginning to race as she probed the most sensitive part of his life and past. She watched the tightening of his hands around the edges of the white china plates. She watched his eyes grow dark and stormy.

"He was killed in a plane crash."

"Were you with him?"

Travis put the plates down with a clatter, the toast sliding around the edge and almost onto the table. "Cat, I don't want to talk about it. Let's just drop it, okay?"

Cathy took a deep breath. She tensed all inside at his harsh, uncompromising tone. "Were you?" she asked softly.

"Cathy . . ." Travis bit out in a hard warning, a cord in his neck pulsing and standing out.

"Were you?" she asked again, even more softly.

Cursing under his breath, Travis slammed a fist down on the back of his chair. "Yes!" he shouted. "Yes, I was with him! *I* piloted the plane. *I* brought it down, and it hit a building, starting a fire. *I* was the one who got out to get help, and Mitch was left trapped in his seat."

"Travis—"

"You wanted to know, so let me finish, dammit! I didn't try hard enough. The engine blew, and Mitch died! I watched my brother die and did nothing about it. That's what I dream about. I'm responsible!"

Cathy let him shout at her, let him use her as a sounding board for feelings she suspected had been bottled up for a very long time—too long. He blamed himself, but with every fiber of her being Cathy knew beyond any doubt in her mind that he couldn't be at fault. The Travis she'd come to know didn't desert people in time of need. Not willingly. And as awful as his experience had been, Cathy sensed that there was more to his anguish and nightmares.

"No one can blame you, Travis. I know—"

"It *was* my fault. Don't you understand? I shouldn't have left him alone," he ground out, his face tight and pinched, the area around his mouth pale and drawn with his tension. Cathy felt deep compassion and concern for him, and if he hadn't been wound up as tightly as a coiled spring, she would have instinctively put her arms around him. He'd been carrying this grief around for an eternity. It explained so many things about him.

"Travis, I've seen Melinda. There was no evidence that she blames you. Does she?"

Travis closed his eyes, shaking his head, a deep sigh escaping. "No, she doesn't. Melinda—Melinda understands. Maybe better than I do. Who knows—"

"What about the rest of your family? Surely the hurt and sorrow have passed?"

Travis opened his eyes now to look at her, but the sharp stare was vacant and lost to some other scene, maybe another person. Cathy wondered with a chill of dread if Travis was perhaps thinking of his ex-wife.

"I wouldn't know," Travis said tiredly, almost in defeat. "I—I haven't been home in in four years."

Four years! My God, all that time? was the thought that went through Cathy's head. Four long, horrible years of living with pain over one family member and his alienation from the rest. What kind of family did he have that found it so hard to forgive?

Travis blinked out of his reverie and focused on Cathy. He began to frown at her, his eyes sweeping over her as she stood anxiously in front of him. She registered. The pregnancy registered. What had happened registered. "Oh, God..." Travis groaned emotionally. He turned away to the bedroom.

"Travis?" Cathy called after him, but he ignored her. By the time Cathy followed him, Travis was already leaving the room. He had on his shoes and was tucking a red polo shirt into the waist of his jeans. "Travis?"

He walked past her, looking for his jacket, for his keys and log books. "My father used to tell me often enough what a lousy son I was—how irresponsible."

Cathy gasped. "I don't believe he meant that!"

"Maybe he was right. Maybe I really don't know how to think of other people, to care about them."

"Oh, Travis, that's not true!" She was frantic, wanting to get through to him and have him believe her. "I don't believe that of you!" He stopped abruptly and turned to glare at her.

"Then maybe you should," he said in a harsh, cold tone. "I haven't done you much good, have I?"

Cathy's plea for him not to go was lost in the opening of the door and its sharp closing as Travis did leave the apartment. Cathy stared at the door, wondering where he was going, what he would do. Would he come back? Tears blurred her vision and spilled down her cheeks. It hurt her that he believed such awful things of himself. How could his family not love him still? How could he believe that no one could? She did....

Cathy turned with drooping shoulders back to the room behind her. She looked fixedly at the set table, the ready breakfast, now cold and uneatable. She was no longer hungry. The tears flowed freely. And she made the emotional, totally irrelevant decision that she could never have breakfast again if she couldn't have it with him.

CATHY AGAIN STOOD staring at the table. It was set anew for two people. This time for dinner. During the whole afternoon of reminiscing about their odd relationship, Cathy continued to believe that Travis would come back, that he simply needed time alone to handle his own painful past and present confusion. She wanted a chance to tell him how very important he was to her. Maybe it took the threat of his really leaving for Cathy to see that. How could she not, she thought ruefully, love someone who could brave with her the indignity of being sick to her stomach, as she had been weeks before, or who was prepared to hand-feed her when she stubbornly refused to eat?

It was seven o'clock. Cathy's dinner, planned and prepared with newly discovered hope and love, simmered and was kept warm in the kitchen. And wanting everything to be right, just in case, she showered and changed into a simple aquamarine sundress with thin shoulder straps. She brushed and fluffed her hair, clipping the curls away from the sides of her face with white barrettes. She applied a bit of makeup and slipped on white low-heeled sandals. All the time she dressed she thought of Travis, remembering that first night when he'd come back drunk. Cathy hoped he wouldn't do that to himself again.

When she was all ready, Cathy sat on the love seat and waited. An hour later, just when she was about to give up in despair, a knock came at the door. Even though she'd been waiting, the sound startled her. With her heart pounding, she walked slowly to the door and opened it.

Travis stood gazing down at her, pretty much the same as she'd seen him when he'd left the morning before. The anger and stiffness were gone, perhaps having burned themselves out, and were replaced by an exhausted look around his gray eyes. He hadn't shaved in two days, and that was evident. His eyes were a bit bloodshot, and she wondered where he'd slept, if at all. And though he may have been drinking, he was sober now.

Travis was surprised at the change in her. Not just the pretty dress or different hairdo or the bright red lip coloring that evoked an instant desire to kiss her, but there was a new calm and presence, a new strength that he sensed in her.

Cathy stepped aside, and he came into the apartment. From behind his back Travis sheepishly produced a bouquet of flowers. Cathy's mouth opened in surprise, and she looked up at him with her eyes happy and bright, unquestioning and uncensoring. Her brightness dissolved all of Travis's awkwardness.

"Oh, Travis! They're beautiful! Thank you," she said in awe, realizing at once the honor he was paying her. It was so simple and so romantic. It gave further life to Cathy's hopes and expectations. She buried her nose momentarily in the lush fragrance of the flowers.

Travis braced his hands on his hips, looking her up and down, taking in the fact that she was dressed specially. "I—I suppose you're going out?" he both stated and questioned.

Cathy's eyes widened, and she smiled at him, sensing the curiosity and veiled anxiety. "No, I wasn't going anywhere." She looked down at herself and back to Travis's alert face. "I was waiting for you."

Travis raised a brow as he visibly relaxed. "How did you know I'd be back?" he asked wryly.

Cathy tilted her head up and looked into his eyes. "I hoped you would," she answered honestly in a soft voice.

Travis allowed the caressing tone to wash over him, refresh him, and he lifted a corner of his wide mouth. "Dressed like that? I didn't know I rated so high," he drawled flippantly, but there was uncertainty in the remark.

Cathy started to respond to that and changed her mind. "It—it's a celebration. I sold another article today, and I think the editors want me to do more for them in the future." Then, for a moment, she became shy with Travis and lowered her eyes, her fingers playing with the petals of one flower. "I... was waiting to share the news with you." When she looked up again after there was no response from him, she found Travis staring at her, his eyes searching hers. She couldn't really read his expression. It could have been pleasure or disbelief. It could have been surprise.

Travis looked past her into the living room at the cozy table setting. He began pulling the red polo shirt from his pants as he stepped forward and bent to ply a gentle quick kiss from her surprised mouth. "I'll be ready in fifteen minutes," he said softly, moving off to the bathroom. The door closed, and Cathy stood listening a moment to the start of the shower. Holding the flowers carefully, she went in search of a container.

When Travis emerged later from the bedroom, he was showered, shaved and freshly dressed in navy blue slacks and a cream-colored shirt. Cathy was just coming from the kitchen with a covered dish but stopped in the doorway as they once again quietly looked at each other. "Cathy," Travis began in his deep voice, "I just want to—"

"You don't have to say anything, or explain, Travis. I understand."

Travis could really believe now that she did. She had never been outwardly angry or condemning of him.

"I did worry about you last night. I—I guess you just needed time to think."

"I guess," he replied, sweeping his hand through his hair.

"Would you like something to eat now?" Cathy smiled softly at him as she placed a dish on the table.

He let out a sigh. "Yes, I would."

"Good..." She headed for the kitchen again. "I just need to get—"

"Cat?"

She stopped instantly at his use of the pet name.

"I'm really pleased about the article," he said sincerely, coming closer to where she stood.

She laughed shortly. "You get part of the credit, you know."

"I doubt it," Travis muttered darkly. "But I would like to do something special."

"You already have. The flowers, remember?"

Travis shook his head. "That was an apology. But I thought maybe tomorrow you'd come up with me."

Cathy blinked, her lips parting.

"I thought you'd like to see your clouds up close and firsthand."

Her cheeks were flushed, and her dark eyes sparkled joyously. Travis was momentarily stilled with the extraordinary lovely and appealing picture she made.

"Would you like that?" he asked hesitantly.

Cathy's smile lit up her face. "Oh, Travis! I'd *love* it!"

Chapter Ten

The Cessna-150 stayed low on its course, leaving Cathy and Travis betwixt and between. Below was the ocean undulating in its tidal currents, speckled with seacraft of every size and description. Above them was the sky, pure, clear and a pale blue in color. But where they flew, in this middle air, were the clouds. Rolling, billowing, fluffy and all that Cathy had imagined they would be.

The small two-seater plane was noisy, and conversation was impossible. All of Cathy's exclamations were lost in the droning of the engines. But her open expression, her rosy cheeks and exploring eyes, the soft hand occasionally tapping his arm to gain his attention as she pointed out some new treasure, were communication enough for Travis. A third of his attention was on Cathy's excitement, reliving in her present joy the thrill he'd first experienced when flying in a small plane. Another third of his attention was on his headphone and its aired messages and signals. And the rest was on the uneasy knowledge that Cathy was the first person to fly with him since the crash with Mitch four years earlier.

Travis's invitation to her the night before had been as much a surprise to him as it had been to Cathy. The moment the words had been spoken, his palms had begun to sweat, and his heart lurched against his chest wall. But he'd been sincere. He wanted Cathy to come with him. He wanted to surprise her with the glory of being airborne just high enough to see the details of the earth below. He wanted to give her the obvious pleasure she enjoyed now of a fantasy come true. But he was scared. Scared—terrified came closer to the truth—that something would go wrong as it had before with Mitch.

Weeks ago when Travis had contacted the Miami bureau to ask for a short assignment there to take care of personal business, they had been surprised but not concerned. They recognized that Travis Hoyt was something of a maverick, but he was still their best pilot and their most knowledgeable one in meteorology. Though much of the weather scanning was now done with orbiting atmospheric satellites launched by NASA, computerized and sophisticated, they couldn't always tell the bureau what Travis could tell them purely from his natural sense of air and sea peculiarities. That Travis also sought to fly under unnecessarily hazardous conditions at times was also a puzzle to them, but not of tremendous concern. It was manic. It was almost like a test of willpower, courage and perseverance. Yet they also knew with unquestioning confidence that Travis would never knowingly jeopardize himself or an assignment to his predilection for danger.

They could not know, of course, to what extent he actually used willpower each time he climbed into the cabin of a plane and took control. It was like forcing someone back into the water after nearly drowning. He was continually proving to himself that he was a good pilot and that the accident that had taken his brother's life and left himself so badly scarred, physically and emotionally, had been just that—an accident. When Travis was away from his plane, from the freedom of the open skies and the clear air—in the nighttime when he was a prisoner to his dreams—he was never sure. So the proving and exorcism went on...and on.

Yet the reality was, he was here with Cathy, and his excitement, for entirely different reasons, was almost as great as her own. For somewhere in the back of his mind was the idea that maybe he could one day go back to Boston and make his peace with his father and the past.

Travis pulled the throttle back a little and banked the plane to the right, changing direction. He caught a brief glimpse of Cathy's hand resting against her stomach and wondered anxiously if she was getting motion sick. He'd forgotten about that possibility and questioned instantly if he should take her down. But as Cathy herself caught sight of Miami and recognized landmarks, she turned excited eyes to Travis, her smile soft and joyful, and his concern slipped away.

The joy the flight gave Cathy was indescribable. First, there was the prospect of actually being so close to a phenomenon of nature that she felt she could have reached right out and touched a cloud. Then there was the experience of being in a light plane, so that her sense of flying and her feeling of being afloat on air was enormousy heightened. But beyond even this exhilaration was the fact of being with Travis.

Their strange life together in the apartment had been barely cordial and certainly lacking the total warmth she wanted in a relationship. There were moments, of course, when they both seemed to border on establishing more between them. But the circumstances of their coming together always seemed to place a firm barrier to anything deeper developing.

That day and the dinner the night before had been the first real occasions of activity and closeness between them that didn't touch on her pregnancy or on their mutual concern as to how to best deal with it. It was just the two of them, and Cathy found it heavenly. She loved the masculine picture Travis made as he commanded the small Cessna, speaking expertly and confidently to the control tower as he checked his plane and conditions for takeoff. His aviator glasses were a shield against the sun, hiding his catlike eyes but making his face appear strong and rugged and in total control. He'd explained that the Cessna belonged to a colleague at the weather service. But Cathy knew that even if they'd been together on a bike built for two, she would have been just as happy. The absolute joy of the trip was in making it with him. Words and images of descriptive pleasure went through her head, and Cathy laughed softly at the poem taking definite form.

As the plane circled wide over the Miami area, Travis attempted to point out places of interest below, shouting above the sound of the engines so forcefully that the cords stood out in his neck. After a time, Cathy began to make signals to him. He frowned when he interpreted them to mean she wanted to go down. Travis's arms tensed.

"Are you all right?" he shouted.

Cathy smiled and nodded. "Yes," she yelled back. "But can we go down? Our picnic... what about our picnic?"

Travis nodded in understanding and once more gave his attention to the plane. He looked around him, trying to remember all the area and where they might freely put down for an hour or so. He swung the plane north, and just west of the Seminole Indian reservation he began to descend to a strip of land bordering on the reservation and the Big Cypress National Preserve. The land, while relatively flat, was rough with undergrowth and grass, spotted with patches of weed water. The plane came to a halt after a few bumps and Travis cut the engines. He turned to face Cathy, slowly taking off his dark glasses, his eyes suddenly startling and eerie in his tanned face. He, in turn, enjoyed the picture she made, her pretty face framed in her curls, her color healthy and glowing, her lips pink from the gentle gnawing of excitement.

"That—that was just wonderful!" Cathy breathed, smiling brightly at him.

"Was it everything that you expected?" Travis asked in amusement, secretly pleased to have given her such simple pleasure.

"Oh... even better!" She laughed lightly, and then, taking them both by surprise, she leaned forward against his chest and planted a kiss on his smiling mouth. "Thank you," she whispered. "It was a wonderful present."

Their eyes widened and locked together, and Cathy held her breath as she watched him, though not really surprised by her own actions. Travis's eyes grew intense, and confused by the sudden expression of hard control in his face, Cathy quickly pulled back, embarrassed now by her spontaneity.

Travis was not embarrassed. It had just taken all of his efforts not to crush her to him and accept her thanks in full measure. He was still sure she was not yet ready for the full extent of his feelings. "Let's have lunch," he said more brusquely than he meant, but Cathy withdrew from him, biting her lip in consternation. Travis silently cursed his clumsiness and uncertainty, wishing he knew how to bring back the light to her eyes, the ready smile to her beautiful mouth.

With his hands on her waist, Travis lifted Cathy from the plane's cockpit and reached behind her seat for the tote that contained their lunch and a blanket and the inevitable notebook she took with her everywhere. Carrying the bag, Travis located a spot on a dry piece of land some distance from the plane, at an equal distance from an old dilapidated shack in the other direction. There was grass that was warm, having already known the benefit of early-afternoon sunlight. Cathy's spirits began to lift again; she was determined to enjoy the day to its fullest.

Travis spread the large blanket out and stood awkwardly watching as Cathy knelt and began taking things out and spreading them about. Travis also felt decidedly foolish, not having any idea what was expected of him now. Cathy looked up at him and gave him a shy squinting smile against the sun. "I suppose you think I'm being silly, wanting a picnic and all, but it's been a very long time since I had one." Relaxing at her confession, Travis lowered his tall body next to her and rested a forearm over his one bent knee.

"I don't think it's silly, I just haven't had much experience myself. I'm not sure what I should do."

Cathy relaxed, as well, and sat back on her heels, grinning at him. She was wearing a boat-neck cotton striped shirt in white and pink and a pair of rose-colored cotton slacks. She looked very summery and lovely. Travis inwardly enjoyed her nearness and renewed cheerfulness, particularly pleased that he might be responsible.

A curl had looped low over her left eye, and Travis reached a hand up slowly to brush it aside. His eyes traveled leisurely to her mouth and back to her bright brown eyes.

"It's very easy," Cathy said. "All you have to do is eat, enjoy yourself and watch out for the ants!"

Travis grinned, raising a brow, his face changing and

opening up youthfully to join in her good time. "We're not likely to find ants here. But if it gets wet, there'll be mosquitoes all over the place!"

"It wouldn't dare rain!" Cathy growled playfully. "This is *our* picnic, and it better not."

Travis laughed quietly at her threat and settled back to rest the weight of his upper body on bent elbows. Yet he was concerned. He'd thought it best not to tell Cathy that the prettier the clouds, the more chances there were for a quick shower. The ocean's warmth right now quickly evaporated the seawater into rain clouds. This plus the easterly rotation of the earth moved the clouds counterclockwise with prevailing air currents. It was a perfect setup for a condition that made daily rains in parts of Florida normal. But Travis sensed from the size and kinds of clouds, which were for the moment so picturesque, that much more than a shower was possible that day. He only hoped he could get them back to Miami before the worst of the storm broke.

Cathy had put together several sandwiches, but there were also salads, cheese, fresh fruit, chilled beer for Travis and lemonade for herself. They ate quietly, with Cathy asking questions for the first time about his work and how he got started flying. Travis answered rather somberly—so much of the past was part of what he was doing now—but the painful reticence of two days ago was gone. And pursuing her tactics of two days earlier, Cathy casually asked where he was really from. She watched a cloud of emotion briefly shadow his green eyes and then disappear.

"Boston," Travis responded shortly.

"Did you grow up on a houseboat there?" she asked.

Travis lifted a corner of his mouth in dry humor. "It was something substantially bigger," he said cryptically, recalling the modern ranch house with its thirteen rooms that was home. Then, with amusement dawning, Travis saw that Cathy didn't realize or suspect that he might be someone of financial means. He wondered what her reaction would be to knowing his family owned a large corner of the state of Massachusetts.

Cathy wanted to ask Travis about his brother and father

again but dared not, since it was apparent to her that it was still a touchy subject and something he hadn't resolved. She wished she could say to him that he had to believe with his heart and not his head that his family would always love him. It would lead him to see that whatever hurt or disappointment might have happened between them in the past could never be enough to let them lose one of their own.

Together, after eating, they put everything away. And while Travis lay drowsily with his head pillowed in his folded arms, Cathy explored the site around their blanket, enjoying the bird sounds and the smell of the nearby cypress trees in the hot, humid air, unaware that Travis's eye followed her protectively until she finally returned to the blanket. Sighing in contentment, Cathy pulled out her notebook, sat down next to Travis's prone body and began to write.

Travis's eyes were closed against the sun, but he could feel it on his lids. For a long time he lay and let the sensation seep into him until he was totally aware of the warmth of his body. It was sometimes intermittent as a cloud moved in front of the sun momentarily and as, out of the corner of his closed eyes, he could detect the darkening of the sky.

For a long time Travis was still. It occurred to him that he couldn't remember the last time he'd just rested idly in the sun for no reason other than the pure lazy enjoyment of it. He could feel every point at which his body touched the earth, because he was suddenly totally relaxed. Travis squinted one eye open to a mere slit and with a small move of his head found Cathy at his side. He could only see part of her face, her square jaw and the full curve of her mouth. Her eyes were gazing off somewhere in the distance as she bit thoughtfully on the end of her pencil eraser. For a fleeting moment Travis envied Cathy her ability to see the world through trusting, forgiving eyes. Or just her ability to make the best of harsh, unexpected realities. He wondered, too, why she continued to have anything to do with him, why she let him stay. He sometimes expected her to turn from him in defense of his sometimes brusque behavior toward her or to send him packing along with his nightmares, but she never did. She only gave him understanding and time—more than he had a right to hope for. It was hard to say to her that his own sense of inadequacy and insecurity left him paralyzed to do much more than he did.

A slight humid wind rushed through Cathy's glossy hair and set the curls tumbling about her cheek and neck. Travis absently reached up a hand and wove his long, slightly calloused fingers into her hair until he could feel her scalp. Cathy didn't jump or demonstrate surprise at the contact but turned her head to him. She looked down into the relaxed rugged face, into the light eyes, soft and curious, as he studied her.

"I thought you were asleep," she whispered, smiling at him. She pushed her pencil and paper aside.

Travis's response was to apply pressure to the back of her head, gently but purposefully bringing her down to him. Her lips parted in definite surprise now, but she allowed herself to come against him, half across his chest until their faces were only inches apart. Cathy could feel the heat from the sun on his white shirt and on the fabric of his jeans. The incredible tan of his skin was enhanced in color and warm, as well. She could feel the virile strength in his stretched-out body but could see that other softening in him that she had been witness to several times before. It was an appealing element to his manliness that sometimes made him, as it did right now, touchable.

"What are you writing?" he drawled in a deep lazy tone.

"N-nothing much." She hesitated, again not daring to let him know it was about him. "Just a few notes and ideas."

Travis raised a corner of his mouth, his fingers in her hair a caressing massage on her scalp, sending a languid stirring sensation down her spine. "Writing about clouds again?"

"No," she answered softly, suddenly fascinated with the closeness of his mouth. She wondered if he was going to kiss her. She wanted him to.

Travis released her head, and his hand slid to her neck, her shoulders, down her back, to rest in the swooping curve between her waist and buttocks. His fingers worked their way under the hem of her sweater to lay on the smooth skin. With his other hand Travis playfully pulled and flicked at the curls over her forehead. The gesture was so personal and friendly that Cathy felt herself melting completely toward him and dared to believe that he might begin to truly care for her. She placed her hands on his chest complacently.

"There's more food in the bag," she murmured absently for want of anything else to say as they silently gazed at each other and unspoken feelings began to grow between them. "Would you like another sandwich? I—I think there's an orange—"

"Shh," Travis said more with the motion of his curved mouth than with sound. His eyes traveled her face slowly and carefully, the gray-green lights missing nothing in her expression. "I don't want a sandwich." His finger moved across her mouth, his eyes following the action and picking up on her response of moistening her lips with the tip of her tongue. His jaw tensed. "Or an orange."

Cathy's heart pounded now in anticipation, willing him on.

Travis dragged his eyes up to hers. "I think I'd rather have you," he said in a husky voice.

There was a long pause until their stillness was broken by Travis reaching to gently capture her mouth with his and gently pulling away. Their breaths mixed. The feel made Cathy hold her breath as she waited for more. His free hand curved around her neck, rubbing the soft fine skin until Cathy felt the tingling begin again. The pressure of his hand pulled her within easy reach so that his mouth could play and tease, his tongue flick and stroke, until he'd manipulated her mouth the way he wanted. When he finally kissed her again, a deep, almost inaudible sigh left her completely pliant.

Cathy closed her eyes and let the quivering warmth produced by his touch ripple through her alert body.

She became lost in the mastery of his kiss, the texture

of his tongue and lips, the expert movement as he rocked eloquently over her own. She became dizzy, lost in the delicious embrace. Cathy was so glad that at least kissing her had not been part of his original promise. But the potency of his effect on her now made her want to wish the promise unspoken and away altogether.

Travis felt the change in her response, felt the acquiescence and guessed at the growing need. With a low groan of triumph in his throat, he suddenly shifted and moved, swinging over to bring Cathy onto her back, with him on top of her. Then his kiss changed, too. It deepened and demanded, suddenly giving and showing her all the feelings that he'd kept in check for the past two weeks. He was in turn tender and passionate, questing and taking until Cathy's hands were squeezing at his shoulders and her slender body shook under the hardening demand of him.

Suddenly, there was a low, distinct grumbling of thunder over their heads to the west. Travis did not really hear it now, but Cathy's body reacted at once, jerking and going still against him. The gasping breath she took made their mouths separate. Travis dragged his mouth down to kiss the hollow of her throat.

"Travis," Cathy whispered brokenly, moving her head as he tried to take her mouth again. His deep green eyes were questioning, but Cathy only tried to wriggle out from under him. The rolling thunder came again, louder, and with it an almost instant darkening of the sky. Cathy's growing agitation brought Travis alert, and he quickly rolled away and sat in front of her. Fat heavy drops of water were beginning to come down. The air grew steamy, the humidity level even higher.

Travis stood cursing under his breath, angry that he hadn't responded more quickly. He pulled Cathy to her feet and passed her the tote, throwing her writing things in on top. He yanked the blanket from the ground and looked around him. They were too far from the plane; in any case, he couldn't take off on the rough terrain in the rain, which was beginning to come down hard. Travis looked carefully around him several times and turned to Cathy, who stood huddled and still and absolutely pale with her own private terror of the moment. Travis had no time now to reassure her. He had to get to the plane and the radio.

"Look," Travis said, pushing the blanket into her arms, "I have to leave you for a while. Make for that shack over there for cover. This shouldn't last too long."

Cathy didn't move, although her eyes widened in alarm at his mention of leaving her. The thunder cracked through the air, and the rain came harder. Her hands clenched the blanket to her chest, and she closed her eyes tightly. The water matted her summer clothing to her body. Travis could see exactly what was happening and knew the first thing was to get her out of the rain. Clenching his teeth against what he had to do right now, Travis turned her by the shoulders in the direction of the hut and pushed her forward.

"Move!" he said roughly. "It's going to get worse!"

Cathy stumbled once and then began running for the shack, her head bowed low against the rain. Travis watched her for a moment and then ran off toward the plane. The rain was pouring down now, thundering heavily into the earth, creating swamplets and puddles, slowing his progress and making it hard to see.

Travis got to the plane, started the engines and taxied down the stretch of land to within a hundred feet of the shack. The radio told him the current reports on air traffic and what backups existed in the Miami area, which planes were advised to wait before flying in or what outlying airfields to use instead. The direction of the storm he could figure out himself.

He turned the plane around, placing it in a position for takeoff, and cut the engines again. Travis jogged quickly to the hut but was still totally soaked when he reached it. There was no door, and one wall of the two-room structure was completely gone. The rain slanted into the opening, lessening the available dry space. Part of the roofing was also gone, but the wooden floor was intact, and whatever else there was left was solid.

"Cathy?" Travis called when he ducked into the low, lopsided doorway, his fingers combing his hair out of his face and eyes. "Cathy?" he called again, anxious now, and only finally locating her when the thunder roared again and a frightened cry came from deep within the structure.

Travis made his way to a dark, rank corner and found Cathy flat against a wall, her knuckles white as she clutched the blanket they'd picnicked on. She was wet and shivering. When he called her name a third time, her head turned blindly in his direction. Silent tears were rolling down her pale cheeks from eyes that were positively glazed and dilated with fear. Travis felt a tight constriction in his chest at what she was going through. She looked so much like a little girl in that instant and very badly frightened. Her hair was in sleek ringlets falling over her forehead into her face and eyes. Her eyes themselves were round and enormous.

Slowly, Travis came to her, keeping his eyes locked to hers. He began to murmur to her, calling her name. He gently put out his hands to take her arms and felt the trembling all through her.

"Cat," he said softly, pulling her into his arms and cradling her against his chest. Travis took the blanket and put it around himself, and holding her close, enfolded her within the rest of it, cocooning them together. She buried her face into his wet shirt. Travis remembered having done this before, and all he did now was hold and stroke her securely, feeling her body tense with each additional sound from the sky until out of pure exhaustion she stopped trembling and the fright wore itself out. Travis sank to his knees, bringing her limp body with him, and she fell forward against him.

"I'm here, sweetheart. I won't leave you again," he said fervently.

He held her through the transitions of the storm for more than an hour until the rain finally stopped. Standing up once more and as quickly as he could, Travis got them back to the plane and, airborne, headed for Miami. There was total silence from Cathy, who sat numb and trancelike. She moved when she was told but said nothing, all energy and feeling for the time being washed out of her. Helplessly, Travis wondered what had happened to cause her such fright in a storm. He had come to see Cathy as someone with considerable strength and vitality, perhaps instilled from her innocent perception of the basic good in life and a belief that there was nothing to deliberately hurt or hinder her. But something, at some time, somewhere, had done her harm, making her vulnerable.

They made it back to the apartment in the same silence, with Travis having to lead her all the way. Her stupor seemed to be founded now mostly in weariness, and Travis thought that if she just got some rest, she would come out of it. He practically undressed her himself and got her into the warm, dry bedding. With a deep sigh, Cathy fell asleep at once.

He was afraid to leave her again, afraid to have her wake up alone. Travis nervously paced the living room, smoking one cigarette after another, constantly looking in on her as she slept. He wondered what good he was doing her, upsetting her life, giving her nothing but pain and unhappiness, turning her simplest pleasures into disasters. Travis began to think miserably that perhaps it would be better, at least for Cathy, if he just got out of her life and left her alone. She could have the abortion, Travis thought painfully, and forget all about him. She could go on with her life the way she'd planned. Yet he wasn't sure if he could survive losing her now.

Finally, Travis undressed, and he, too, got into the bed next to her, only to lay in the dark, watching her in sleep. He slid very close to her in the bed and gently settled a large hand on her abdomen, just because he felt the need to touch her. Her breathing was even and peaceful, her skin smooth and warm under his fingers, her natural color returned. Some of his pent-up anxiety escaped in a shuddering sigh.

Once Cathy sighed and moved her hand to her midriff. When her fingers encountered Travis's hand, her fingers curled lightly around his wrist, and she slept on. Travis watched her, loving the now-healthier flush to her countenance and her disarray of curls—loving her. It was after midnight when Cathy sighed languidly and opened her eyes. Travis was still observing her closely.

Cathy blinked at finding him so close and at realizing that they were both in bed naked. She noticed more, however, a bleak torment in Travis's face, the grim line of his mouth, the total weariness in his stormy eyes. She reached out a soft hand to stroke his cheek and smile softly at him. Travis turned his head to kiss the heel of her hand where it rested near his mouth.

Cathy herself felt oddly settled and rested. She felt inside as if she had indeed survived a violent storm, and now she was going to be all right. "You look so sad," she observed sleepily.

"I was worried about you," Travis responded hoarsely, but swallowed his relief at the clarity and sparkle in her eyes. He wondered if she remembered what had happened.

"Are we home?" she asked in some confusion.

"For hours," Travis said, taking her hand to hold it. "Don't you remember?"

Cathy closed her hand around the kiss he'd given her lovingly and gazed at him. "I remember...the storm. Chad leaving me...." She blinked with a frown. Travis was alert but puzzled by the reference to her brother. Or did she mean himself? "I remember you finding me," she whispered, her eyes softening on him.

Travis's fingers explored her stomach. Cathy watched his face, smiling at him again. She was pleased with the emotions she read in him now, pleased that they were for her and hopeful that it meant more. She'd always believed that Travis stayed with her out of a sense of guilt for her and that whenever the question of her pregnancy was settled, he would leave. He was a loner by choice. Heroes are. Nothing would hold him still that he hadn't decided on himself. That she loved him was part of her romantic nature, which said that fate more than circumstances had brought them together, therefore, perhaps it was her destiny that with him she would grow up, be a woman, become a mother. The thought was not as frightening as it had been. Perhaps Elizabeth Harris was right and love was enough. And if there was a chance that Travis would eventually leave, then she'd have her love and their miracle together—and the little time now in the dark with him.

"Cathy," Travis began. "About the storm. I didn't mean to scare you. But I had to leave you like that." Travis had a momentary heart-stopping flash of Mitch in a burning plane.

"I'm not scared anymore," Cathy said, and again Travis was puzzled by her words. "When you were holding me, I was fine."

Travis tried to understand her. She was fully awake and herself again. Their gaze held as slowly, deliberately, Cathy pushed the sheet that was covering her away, exposing her full rounded breasts and their creamy tan nipples. They were softly erect, rising and falling with her breathing. The sheet was left bunched on her thighs, showing Travis's hand still resting protectively on her and the rest of her naked body and his.

Travis's eyes shone bright and expectant as he leisurely took in her flushed slender body. His eyes rose to meet hers. Cathy smiled even more, as if sure of herself. Travis hoped he was reading her correctly. He hoped that what he was feeling from her was real. He wanted to make love to her badly. He'd started to that afternoon, willing to risk her rejection of him. But he remembered that Cathy had been totally responsive, firing his blood and enticing him on with her answering kisses and caresses, giving him hope. But it seemed ironic that what had happened so naturally and easily the first time between them in April had become a strained near-impossibility now.

Watching her face, Travis let his hand rise up from the slight curve of her stomach to her breast. He cupped it slowly, sliding the hand over the silky skin until his fingers brushed over her nipple. Cathy sighed, and Travis's hand rode with the movement. He took it gratefully as encouragement and moved toward her, bending to kiss her. Cathy's hand slid up his muscular arm to his shoulder, found the nape of his neck and gently urged him down.

"Cathy," Travis murmured, putting his arms around

her. She arched her body against his for more complete contact, feeling his heat and strength against her. Travis began to kiss her with a need and hunger that quickly ignited them both. He tossed the covers completely aside, and with a reverence that made his hands shake at first, explored her body. He stroked and stimulated in secret little places, ravaging her senses and eliciting delightful little sounds.

It was almost like the first time in that there was surprise and exultation—the little discomfort that confirmed for Travis that no one else had had her since that time and then, with slow gentleness, easing again into an ecstasy that stripped their lungs of air and made them cling and move together passionately as one.

The summer heat and exertion dampened their bodies, leaving them sultry. They were both totally giving, yielding, wanting to please. The sharing was perfectly timed and equally explosive. Cathy tried to form the words that would have told him of her love but couldn't. And Travis never gave her a chance, kissing the words and murmurings away until she could only concentrate on his hands and mouth. Sparked by the long wait and uncertainty between them, Travis made love to her again before he finally let her sleep, curled against him, breathing in the lovely, sweet essence of her.

For whatever reasons, it occurred to Travis that he no longer had any clear idea what he'd felt for his ex-wife, Cathy. It was certainly nothing like what he felt for and with Cathy now. Even from the first there was an affinity between them. Perhaps not understood, even now, but tangible and real. It left him fiercely protective and humble. Perhaps with his wife it was little more than rebellious youth, pride, lust and immaturity. It had never been love. Everything else had grown and developed in his life—except love.

Travis gave it a lot of thought in the small quiet space between their lovemaking, as he gently touched and stroked Cathy's body to reassure himself. It seemed to him now that the way to healing and forgiveness, to the restoring of his faith, his very soul—his self-respect—the way to the future, out of the past, not seeking with his eyes, which are sometimes blind, and missing what is sometimes invisible, was with the heart and through love.

Travis left a feathery kiss on Cathy's forehead, traveled it down to her cheek and folded her closer to him, closing his eyes. He could sleep now, too, because he'd found the answer he was seeking. The only way to help Cathy and, through her, himself was to love her.

And he did....

Chapter Eleven

Cathy held the paper gingerly by her fingertips as if it were a sacred document, precious and rare. It was. It was a contract handed her by Valerie Banner, commissioning her to do four more articles on subjects relating to women. The contract was enough in itself to leave Cathy speechless; that her opinion on a subject that had only recently led her to ask questions and explore ideas was also considered of value was the added icing on the cake. She was now a professional writer.

Valerie sipped her coffee and watched with interest the awed expression on the face of her luncheon guest. She hadn't expected Catherine Donnelly to appear so young, which made the piece she had written even more phenomenal, because its concept was so mature and well thought out. Valerie thought Cathy looked more like an impish angel than a poet.

Valerie herself was a woman in her late thirties, a little more than pleasantly plump, who'd related personally to Cathy's thesis and remembered her own maturing more than fifteen years earlier when those same questions and ideas of Cathy's weren't asked. There had been an order to things then that wasn't questioned—at least not openly or often. What was good enough for parents was supposed to be good enough for their offspring.

"I know you'll want to go over it, but it's a fairly standard contract."

Cathy stopped scrutinizing the legalese of the contract and smiled at Valerie. She absently hoped that Travis knew how to read a contract and was excited about showing it to him.

Valerie placed both elbows on the table and rested her very rounded chin in her hands. She continued to regard Cathy with curiosity, her pale gray eyes myopic behind large red-framed glasses.

"I read your article in the women's center newsletter," she began casually. But Cathy was at once alerted. It hadn't occurred to her that Valerie would ever see it and perhaps find out so much about her.

"Yes," Cathy said noncommittally, keeping her eyes down on her plate as she lifted her fork, but unable to hide the giveaway blush that tinted her cheeks.

"Well..." Valerie hesitated. "I...also believe it's best to write what you know about firsthand..." She let the opening go.

Cathy lifted some salad to her mouth. Halfway there she put the fork down again and raised dark clear eyes to Valerie. "It was written from experience," she told Valerie clearly. A determination and defensiveness suddenly made her raise her chin. "I—I'm going to have a baby." Cathy bit her lip and frowned slightly. "That is, I'm... pregnant."

"And you're thinking about an abortion?" Valerie supplied quietly, still watching Cathy carefully.

Cathy swallowed. "No," she answered with more conviction than ever before. "I want this baby," she said with a serene smile. But she was instantly reminded of the call she'd received from Elizabeth Harris days before, gently alerting her to the need for continuing medical checkups on her condition. But she'd put off the appointment for a few days, not wanting to miss her luncheon with Valerie. Cathy had promised to be in by the end of the week.

"What about the baby's father?" Valerie ventured to ask. Cathy's head came up sharply.

That was Travis. He's the baby's father. A curious feeling swept over Cathy. It was warm and personal. It was the first time that Travis had actually been put into that context for her. A father—the father of *her* baby—*their* baby.

In that quick instant Cathy gained another insight into the nature of their relationship. It was a lot closer and intimate than she'd imagined it to be, even a short week ago.

"The baby's father..." Cathy repeated in amazement, and had an unexpected fleeting image of Travis holding an infant against his shoulder. His child. Cathy paled as she looked at Valerie. "He wants me to marry him."

Valerie raised her own brows now and tilted her head. "Obviously you've said no. You don't love him?"

Cathy blinked, and her eyes softened discernibly. It was not lost on Valerie. "Oh, but I do love him. It's just—I don't want him to marry me because of the baby. Because he feels responsible. And I'm not even sure if I'm ready to be a mother yet. But if I have an abortion," she whispered with a catch in her throat, "there'll be no reason for him to stay. And if I have the baby, I'll have something we shared, even if he leaves me."

After a long pause, Valerie let out a sigh, adjusted her glasses and took another sip of coffee. "I take it you're still seeing him?"

Again Cathy suddenly blushed. Seeing him...living with him...making love with him. "Yes."

Valerie signaled for the waiter and began fishing for her credit card. "I had an abortion nearly ten years ago," she suddenly blurted out, her voice calm and even.

Cathy stared silently at her.

"My parents tried to talk me out of it. My boyfriend at the time tried to talk me out of it. I had no one to talk to who understood how I felt. I wasn't careful, and it happened. But I didn't want children. I still don't. But I was so confused and so alone.

"I lost twenty-five pounds in about a month afterward." She looked down ruefully at her chunky comfortable body. "Still, it was one of the worst moments of decision in my life. But it was the right one, and I've never regretted it."

Valerie finally looked at Cathy and smiled softly. Whatever torment had possessed her ten years ago, she had passed through and survived. And perhaps she was saying to Cathy, You will, too. It's your life and your decision, and some of us do understand. Cathy slowly returned the smile.

"I... appreciate you're sharing... that with me," Cathy said.

"I'm looking forward to seeing your next piece," Valerie said now, returning easily to the business at hand.

Cathy laughed softly, liking Valerie with the same inclinations that had drawn her to Elizabeth Harris. These women had a very strong sense of themselves as people, and Cathy admired their strengths and convictions. "I hope you won't be disappointed!" she said, relaxing again, their sharing of a moment ago leaving Cathy feeling released and easy with herself.

"I won't be!" Valerie said positively. And they left the restaurant on Biscayne Boulevard.

Valerie left to return to her office, and Cathy, leaving her leased car parked for the time being, walked idly, enjoying one of the rare warm sunny days in Florida when the humidity didn't also make it unbearable. She didn't pay much attention to her direction. There seemed to be much more in her head to hold her attention than what happened along the busy thoroughfare of Miami. Meeting Valerie and receiving the contract had been a tremendous boost to her ego. It seemed so long ago, an age, as a matter of fact, since she'd decided to strike out on her own. So much had happened since. She'd crammed, unwittingly, years' worth of growth into a few months, enlightening her, astounding and surprising her. And not without its low and high points. There was Travis, and there could be, perhaps, his baby.

Recalling Valerie's words reminded Cathy once again that Travis's part in her life now seemed tenable and irrevocable. It was only now that Cathy considered that if she had any idea how Travis felt about her having his baby, it might matter in her decision. But he never mentioned it, never said one way or another and had, now that she thought about it, stopped insisting that she even marry him. Frowning, Cathy gnawed on her lip, trying to decide if that was significant. It was.

Travis now sought to make her love him, not realizing,

of course, that her feelings were already very much beyond their developing physical relationship, which had already created one bond between them. Cathy readily responded to him and never denied him, and this was further proof to Travis that he would have what he wanted in the end. He'd said as much to her.

They'd lain in bed one night, and Travis had begun to kiss her slowly and tantalizingly with the rising passion that was always the prelude to their lovemaking, his original promise to her completely out the window. Cathy had wound her arms around his neck, lifting her hips suggestively and in readiness to his own bold middle, surging impertinently against her. Travis had brought Cathy to the very edge of repletion, only to withhold her final pleasure and his. Cathy had moaned and blinked in a sensual daze at him, whispering his name in a plea and confused by his sudden temperance.

"You will marry me, Cat—eventually," he said confidently, and although Travis turned her over so he could settle her back against his chest and thighs, he didn't make love to her.

Cathy now crossed a street and wandered into a park. There were children everywhere, making use of the many structures to climb on, under, through and over. She watched their energy in fascination, amazed by their fearlessness and apparent immunity to bumps, scratches, tumbles, falls and dirt. They were so free. There was so much she could learn from them—from her own child, perhaps.

Cathy looked into her lap and smoothed a hand over her stomach. Already some of her clothing was tight. Already her body was giving signs in its own special proper way, and soon they would be obvious. She was almost glad she'd promised to go to the center.

First of all she'd have to tell Elizabeth about the cramps. Every time the pain gripped her, Cathy was more convinced it shouldn't be happening. She wasn't sure why, but the baby shouldn't be hurting this way. And she'd kept it from Travis, as well.

Their complete sharing of the bed, however, of the space, of their bodies, Cathy accepted, because she loved him. There was no morality involved in her thoughts. To do so would have been to pass judgment. Their living together was not a right or a wrong but simply what they'd both agreed on as necessary to the circumstances. If some other arrangement could have been decided upon, no doubt it would have been. Also, she still believed she had no means to hold him, not even through the baby, if she so desired. Travis was a traveler and a searcher, even if not a free-spirited one. And he could be gone at any time.

For now, Cathy would have him and love him as he was. She found Travis's lovemaking joyous. He paced her through the stages of passion with his potency, which gave her knowledge, experience and ease with him. They enjoyed touching each other now and did so often. Travis seemed to take particular pleasure in holding her so that he could stroke and caress her stomach, sometimes planting a tender kiss there, as well. The earlier references to crocodiles became a personal warm joke between them. He seemed to enjoy kissing her awake at any hour of the night just for the pure pleasure of it and the feel of her sleepy response.

Sometimes after they'd made love, Travis would lift himself from her trembling body to kneel between her thighs, then bend and place an almost-reverent, gentle kiss on her bent knee and thigh. It was a curious gesture, but one that Cathy always found uniquely intimate. Once he'd come back to the apartment early to find her typing by the window, the light creating an ethereal brightness around her. Travis had pulled her from the chair, lifted her into his arms and taken her to bed with him at three o'clock in the afternoon.

Travis was also highly inventive, teaching her pleasures she never would have thought of herself. When he was awakened one night with her silky back wriggling and snuggling against his chest and stomach, Travis's response had been immediate and demanding. His hand around her had stroked her hip and thighs, had gently squeezed and rubbed her breasts, until Cathy moaned, wanting him to love her. From that position he had, and from that position they'd fallen back to sleep.

And still there was a restlessness in him at times, only confirming her belief that it was just a matter of time before he'd want to leave. She tried desperately to school herself in what seemed inevitable. But Cathy could not know that Travis's restlessness was not to leave her but to settle the rest of his wayward life. He missed his family— his father. He wanted to see him, make things right with him, bring Cathy home to him. But he hadn't a clue as to how to begin to bridge the gap. The ties seemed too long severed. And despite Cathy's earlier assertion to him that one always belonged to one's family, it was not always true that one could go home again.

It was perhaps brought sharply to mind the afternoon he'd taken her flying again, sans his fear for her safety and her fear of storms, since the sky was outrageously clear. Travis had flown them down to the Grand Bahamas, fifty miles off the tip of Florida, for lunch and sunning on a white, nearly deserted beach. The day had been ideal. They had been ideal, behaving like lovers, holding hands and totally at ease with each other for the very first time. The euphoria had lasted all the way back to Miami, to the apartment and as they undressed each other in preparation for making love. Suddenly, the phone rang. It was strange that the call was for Travis. It was Melinda. Travis had cautiously taken the call, and Cathy had discreetly gone to the bedroom out of hearing.

"Hello, Travis!" Melinda said brightly.

"Melinda..." Travis reluctantly acknowledged, looking around for Cathy and slightly irritated that she'd left him alone but knowing he was being unreasonable.

Melinda laughed at his less-than-welcoming tone. "I must be interrupting something!"

Travis made an impatient sound, coloring uncharacteristically nonetheless.

"How are you doing?" she asked now.

"Melinda, you didn't just call me out of the blue to find out how I'm doing."

"No, you're right," she admitted cheerfully. "As a matter of fact, the base called. They wanted to know when you'd be back."

"Oh?" Travis said, now totally alert.

"Something about September storms and a possible hurricane. You'll have to speak to them yourself for a literal translation."

"All right, thanks. I'll give them a call tomorrow."

There was the slightest pause on the line, and Melinda's next question came low and serious and shocking to Travis.

"Is she pregnant?"

Travis stiffened. When he'd left Key West, he'd only told Melinda he had to go to Miami. She had guessed it was to follow Cathy, and he'd later called her to confirm his whereabouts. But Travis had not told Melinda his suspicions at the time. That had been too personal to share with even his understanding sister-in-law. So to have her question it at once now threw him off, but it was totally pointless to deny it.

"Yes," he confirmed, suddenly feeling old, tired and beyond frustration—nearly defeated. There was another pause.

"What are you going to do?" There was concern now in her voice.

Travis sighed and raked his hand through his thick hair. "I want her to marry me. She says no. I think she's considering an abortion, and I'm trying to talk her into waiting." Travis chuckled dryly, completely without humor. "It's what's commonly called a Mexican standoff."

"Oh, Travis..." Melinda clucked in sympathy. "Do you care?"

Travis was still for a moment. He reached blindly for his cigarettes on a stand near Cathy's typewriter and took the time to light one, exhaling deeply. "I think I'm in love with her, Mel. I can't leave her."

"Have you told her? Does she know?"

Travis puffed on the cigarette. "No, I haven't. Cathy's convinced I'm only staying out of a sense of obligation. If I told her I love her right now, she wouldn't believe me any more than when I told her I wanted to marry her. And I do."

"Oh, dear!" Melinda intoned in understanding of the

situation. "Travis, maybe I should stop by and have a talk with her."

"No, Melinda. I appreciate your concern, but don't."

"But she might listen to me. She might believe what I had to say!"

"No!" Travis ground out, and immediately was sorry for his brusqueness. "Look...I know what you're trying to do, but...I'd rather Cathy believed me."

"All right, Travis. If that's what you want."

"That's the way it is!" he corrected, drawing on his cigarette. He changed the subject. "How are the boys?" he asked, referring to his nephews.

"A handful! They keep asking when you're coming back. I wish you hadn't made that promise to take them diving in John Penekamp Park! Ever since they saw that picture of you and Mitch in your gear, that's all I've heard about!"

Travis smiled slowly, even at the mention of his brother. Travis loved to fly almost as much as Mitch had enjoyed scuba diving. "Tell them I haven't forgotten. It'll just have to wait awhile."

"Well, it's okay for now. I'm taking them to see their grandfather, so their minds are on getting to the farm." Melinda's voice trailed off, and again Travis felt a myriad of feelings tearing through him.

"That's a good idea, Mel," he said evenly. "I told you, you should."

"It'll be good for Dad, too. I know he gets lonely."

Travis's jaw tensed, and his sea-green eyes became bleak with images and feelings. "We all do" was his vague comment. Travis sighed and roughly stamped out his cigarette. "Have a good time and tell the boys hello for me. Did you find a buyer for the houseboat yet?" He quickly changed the subject again.

"I think so. Someone called me from Boston. That's one of the reasons I'm going up there. He sounded rather interesting—and young!"

Travis laughed softly. "Good luck!"

"You realize if I sell you'll have to find somwhere else to live?" Melinda reminded him.

Travis shrugged indifferently. "I'll manage."

"Travis? Do you have any messages for your father?"

"No," he said unequivocally.

"But Travis…"

"No messages, Melinda. If I have anything to say, I'll say it myself. Have a good trip."

When Cathy came from the bedroom after the call, it was to find a somber, changed Travis. The excellent mood of the day was lost. And he was lost again, in his own misery. Cathy knew who had called, but she didn't ask why. And when Travis muttered that he had to go for a walk, Cathy didn't try to stop him, recognizing his need to be alone for the moment. Something or someone else had a hold on him now, perhaps a lot tighter than any she could hope to have. She'd watched him go, seeing that his leaving was also a way of escaping his problems, which perhaps had no solution. Maybe she was one of the problems, Cathy had considered with depressing insight.

Travis had returned just after she'd finally gone to bed but before she'd fallen to sleep. He'd come slowly into the room and leaned against the door frame, looking solemnly at her. Cathy had regarded him silently, not knowing what his scrutiny of her might mean and not knowing really how to help him, or even if she could.

But acting on impulse, Cathy threw back the covers, crawled over to the edge of the bed and beckoned him to her. Travis came to stand in front of her as Cathy knelt and silently undressed him. He had let her, searching her face, loving the touch of her soft, slender hands on his chest as she pushed his shirt open and off his shoulders, loving the feel on his hips and thighs as they pushed his slacks and shorts down, loving her leaning close to press tender little kisses to his chest, instantly exciting him with her gentle loving care. Travis had put his arms around her tightly, searching for her mouth with his own, forcing her mouth open so that his tongue could quickly find hers. Then bending her backward onto the mattress, settling on top of her, he made love to her as gently as he could, afraid that otherwise, in showing the full depth of his emotions and love for her, he would injure her.

"I need you," Travis whispered urgently against her mouth, and Cathy thought he meant for the moment and gave him what he wanted.

CATHY STOOD UP from the bench. The idea came to her that she wasn't that far from the airfield that Travis flew in and out of. He would be coming in soon. She'd meet him there, and they'd come back to the apartment together. She rubbed her abdomen absently, easing away the ache. Suddenly, for reasons Cathy couldn't define, a deep feeling of dread, of premonition, hurried her to the airport. She wanted to welcome him back, as if his being away for a day or even a few hours left her lonely and bereft.

As it turned out, Cathy nearly missed him. He was already down, handing a report to the hangar mechanic and heading toward the office. Travis had a sudden sense of someone behind him, and turning his head at the feeling, saw Cathy walking toward him. She waved and smiled cheerfully, and Travis's heart turned over with the overwhelming gladness he felt at seeing her. He stood watching her approach, noting with what self-assurance and confidence she carried herself. Had she changed—in fact, blossomed—because she was pregnant, he wondered. Cathy walked with a feminine seductiveness that was deceptive, because although it was entirely natural, Travis knew her to be unaware of it. She was a woman, fully grown. And a beautiful one at that.

Cathy began to feel shy under Travis's intense scrutiny as she came up to him, wondering what he was thinking. Was he surprised to see her? Happy? Her steps slowed, and her smile became uncertain.

"I—I was in the neighborhood, and I thought I'd come to meet you." She bit her lip.

Travis was pleased. He grinned and raised a brow. "I like the welcoming committee. How come you're in the neighborhood?" He frowned slightly. "Did you walk all the way here?" he asked sternly.

Cathy's expression was impish. "Almost. I left the car in front of the *Miami Magazine* building."

Travis's eyes grew dark. "Well? How did it go?"

Cathy shrugged casually. "Okay, I guess. I have a mere contract to do four more articles."

Travis gave a surprised laugh and, putting his arms around her, lifted Cathy clear off her feet as he kissed her soundly. "Congratulations! Pulitzer Prize next year?" he teased.

Cathy's feet dangled, and she happily anchored her arms around his neck. "I doubt it! I'll be happy just to get in print!" she said laughing.

Travis shrugged, looking into her excited features, now on a level with his face. "Oh, well...at least make us independently wealthy so I can retire and spend my days staring at clouds!"

His sudden reference to the future was totally spontaneous and certainly sincere. But it stilled Cathy, confusing her again. Travis also now realized what he'd said, and his smile became rueful as he slowly lowered her to her feet. They looked at one another quietly.

"I...thought you said watching clouds was silly?" Cathy said.

"I changed my mind" was the cryptic response from Travis as he ruffled the curls at her neck gently. "Let's go home," Travis said, putting his arm around her shoulder and heading off the field.

They walked to pick up the car and headed back to the apartment. After parking, and nearly in front of the building, Travis took her arm and stood in front of her, halting her steps.

"Cat, I wanted you to know...I was happy to see you today. I'm glad you came."

"I'm glad I did, too," Cathy whispered sincerely. Travis cupped her face and bent to kiss her softly, a kiss not of passion but of warm caring and tenderness and genuine affection between them.

"Cathy?" Her name was spoken in what could only be described as a shocked tone. Cathy jumped, and she and Travis turned their heads. Standing to her right was her brother Chad—and Brian. Cathy was so stunned at finding them both there that she stared blankly for several seconds before she colored a deep embarrassed pink. The two men regarded her being held by Travis with guarded curiosity; in Brian's case it quickly changed to open hostility.

"Wh-what are you doing here?" Cathy stammered foolishly, still within Travis's protective hold.

One of the men, tall and athletically built and with curly light brown hair, answered first, deliberately interrupting the other man, who was standing stiff and angry next to him. "You said you would call, Cathy. And you didn't. When I couldn't reach you myself, I got worried. So did Brian," he added smoothly.

Travis had guessed at once that this had to be Chad. The resemblance between sister and brother was obvious in the general shape of the face and the curly hair. He quickly assessed Chad and at once decided that there was less to worry about from him than from the other—Brian. Travis raised a brow as he realized the potential of the situation and slowly stepped a little farther forward of Cathy so that he partially shielded her.

Cathy bit her lip and looked from one to the other of the men facing her, wondering how she could explain being in the arms of a man that neither of them had heard of, much less seen, before.

"Hello, Cathy," the man Brian said tightly. He swung deadly eyes to Travis, who only calmly regarded him with a kind of detached interest.

"Hello, Brian," Cathy answered weakly, and inadvertently took a step closer to Travis. Chad made careful note of the way his sister aligned herself with this stranger and gave more attention now to him.

Travis and Chad might have been the same height, but Chad was a bit stockier and therefore seemed bigger. For no real reason other than male competitive nature, Chad guessed they'd be pretty evenly matched. But Brian, at nearly six foot three, was taller than Travis, and while slender, was not as firmly built.

Brian suddenly made to move forward, and Chad easily put a restraining hand on his arm. "Just wait a minute, Brian," he said calmly. He didn't want any trouble. And he didn't want to interfere in Cathy's life. He just wanted to make sure she was okay. After that it wasn't any of his business. She had to grow up sooner or later. Looking quickly at her now, Chad could see she was fine. He did note some changes, however. She seemed a bit more self-possessed than the dreamy young woman who'd left home. She was not nearly as thin, and it make her look mature. He couldn't think of another way to put it. She was, of course, surprised to see him and Brian, but not flustered or confused.

Cathy looked briefly up at Travis, who was still looking primarily at Brian. "Travis, this is my brother, Chad." Cathy looked at Brian, raising her chin a little. There were two bright spots of color high on her cheek that were actually very attractive at the moment. "And...this is my... this is Brian Radcliff," she finished.

Travis merely inclined his head.

"I don't mean to interfere, Cathy," Chad began, looking back and forth significantly between her and Travis. "But when you didn't call...well...I had to do something."

Travis took a half step closer. "Maybe I can help" came his quiet, deep voice in the chilled atmosphere. "Cathy has been researching information for her writing," Travis smoothly improvised.

Cathy blinked in astonishment, and then she stared at Travis, beginning to feel annoyance build inside her. She didn't want him to lie for her. She didn't need him to protect her, either. "Wait a minute," she said softly, but it was lost in Brian's sharp tone of voice.

"On what?" he asked challengingly. Travis turned a decidedly indifferent glance toward Brian and carelessly looked him up and down, adding fuel to the fire already smoldering.

"On clouds," Travis responded. Chad crossed his arms over his chest, and pursing his lips, looked down at his feet to hide his eyes and reaction.

Brian frowned in disbelief. "Clouds?" he questioned incredulously.

"Yes, clouds!" Cathy responded to his derision, stepping in front of Travis to confront the man glaring at her.

Brian spread his hands. "What the hell good is that?" he questioned, making Cathy feel silly. She drew herself up tall.

"I'm writing a book of poetry. The book *you* always told me was foolish!"

Brian backed off a little from her and turned his displeasure upon Travis. Pointing a finger at him, he said, "And what does he have to do with it? Showing you what it's like on cloud nine, I suppose? Is that what you were doing in his arms?"

Cathy gasped. Travis's jaw tensed, and his hand made a fist at his side.

"Easy, Brian..." Chad warned quietly.

"Brian..." Cathy began, and stopped helplessly, knowing there was never going to be an easy explanation for what he'd witnessed. And she couldn't help feeling she owed him one.

"As a matter of fact, yes!" Travis's voice came bold and hard in the air, his watchfulness gone. His gray-green eyes stabbed at the tall blond man in front of him.

Cathy placed a gentling hand on Travis's arm and felt the hard, bunched muscles. Again Chad was alert to the communication between them. "Brian, you have no right to talk to me that way!"

"Who has a better right—" he swung angrily to her "—than your fiancé?"

Travis, for all intents and purposes, showed no reaction other than a tightening of his mouth and a watchful narrowing of his eyes.

"You belong to me!" Brian said, wretched now.

Cathy looked at him clearly. "I don't belong to anyone but myself. I didn't give myself away to you just because we considered getting married!"

Brian laughed harshly. "It's too late in any case, isn't it, since you've obviously given yourself to *him*!" Again he stabbed a finger at Travis. "Are you living with him as well as sleeping with him?"

Cathy blanched and gasped and was speechless by the truth of it, no matter how nastily expressed by Brian. Travis immediately reacted to intervene protectively, but

Brian suddenly rushed forward, swinging a fist at Travis. Cathy cried out for him to stop but was ignored as the fist caught Travis in that area below his cheek at the corner of his mouth and nose. The impact sent him reeling backward a few feet, but he stayed upright and brushed the back of his hand over his face, finding blood.

Brian stood pleased and poised, ready to swing again as Chad tried to grab his arm. But Cathy moved, trying to get between Travis and Brian, and Chad turned his attention to getting her out of the way.

"Travis!" she cried, frightened.

"Brian, that's enough!" Chad added.

Hearing Travis's name on her lips was enough to fire Brian angrily again. Travis never made a move toward Brian now that he'd collected himself, and he didn't have to. Believing he had the advantage, Brian swung again at Travis. But this time Travis deftly ducked his head to the side and grabbed Brian's arm as it swung past his head. Then what happened next was so fast and neat that no one had time to react to prevent it.

Holding on to Brian's wrist, Travis stepped forward and braced his free arm under Brian's in such a way that with one forceful push from his other hand, Brian's wrist was broken, and a short anguished cry of pain escaped him. Then Travis hooked the heel of his right leg around Brian's left one, and with another simple push, sent Brian backward and onto the pavement in a heap. There was an incredible silence afterward that hung in the air. Chad released his sister and went to help Brian. Cathy also made a half move to his side and stopped as the look of wounded pride, hurt and anger pierced her, sweeping a chill through her body.

Instead she went to Travis, looking anxiously at his bruised face, sorry for the blood and the hurt and the whole mess. Cathy reached up to touch the reddening corner of his wide mouth. Travis's eyes dropped to hers, and they were suddenly dark as he stared. Cathy couldn't read a thing in his face but also felt that same curious chill. She slowly turned to watch as Brian got stiffly to his feet with Chad's help, holding his arm limply in front of his chest. He was suddenly pale beneath his tan, making his skin look strangely jaundiced. His hair was disheveled, as were his clothes. To Cathy, he looked at that moment like a young boy. He looked soft and unconditioned. He looked unused to being anything but immaculate and in control. He looked petulant.

Cathy had fancied she'd always known what Brian was like. But in the realm of one who dreams a lot and suspects that most of the dreams will not come true, she knew that a life with him would have been at least comfortable, if without adventure and excitement. But she knew now she'd never loved him. At least not with the same love that consumed her for Travis and that was so rich and full. She knew that she'd never see Brian again. There was some sadness and regret at the loss. Brian had played his own part in her growing up. But there was no remorse. He was not destined to go into the future with her. Sadly, Cathy thought she had no idea what the future held for her anymore.

After steadying Brian on his feet, Chad began walking back toward his sister, but his eyes were riveted to Travis. Cathy saw the frowning look and immediately misinterpreted it as belligerence. Even Travis, responding to it, stiffened again. Cathy placed herself in front of Travis and pressed back against his chest to stay him.

"Let me talk to him, Cathy," Travis said in his deep voice, starting to move her aside.

"No! Let *me* talk to him. Please, Travis!"

Travis looked down at her tired, drained face and gave in. He just wanted to get her away from this. He looked over her shoulder at her brother, and the two men now silently took each other's measure. When they were through, they both relaxed, and the suspicions melted considerably.

Cathy walked over to her brother and gazed up into his face. It was concerned and protective but not outraged. "I'm sorry Chad. I didn't mean to make you worry. I—I didn't mean for this to happen."

Chad stuffed his hands into his trouser pockets. He nodded and let out the tension he was holding in. "Is

everything okay?'' he asked. Cathy hesitated, thinking of
a response, and finally smiled weakly.

"I'm fine."

"Do you want me to hang around for a while?"

Cathy's smile widened. "No. I'm old enough to take
care of myself. I don't need any help."

Chad's glance bounced off Travis, standing grimly alert
some distance behind Cathy. Cathy tried to answer the
look and the silent question in her brother's eyes without
saying more than she wanted to.

"I'm here with Travis because I want to be, Chad," she
said softly. That was all she said, and he understood.

"I gotta get Brian to a doctor. I expect to hear from you
soon." That was no longer a request but a demand. Cathy
recognized that, and she nodded meekly. Then once more
he looked fully at Travis. Chad made a decision and gave a
barely discernible smile. He patted Cathy's cheek affectionately. "Take care of my sister," he said softly, and
after a pause turned to help a still-glaring but silent Brian
back to the car.

Travis cautiously came up to Cathy as she stood watching her brother drive away. Travis didn't say anything; he
was actually afraid to. But then Cathy looked up at him,
searched his face and with a strength, control and command that was admirable under the circumstances, smiled
at him. Their fingers touched and laced together tightly,
and they began walking wearily into the building.

In the kitchen Cathy took the red bandanna that Travis
always carried and dampened it to wipe the blood from his
face. But after a minute or so, Travis had had enough and
stopped her by taking hold of her wrist. Cathy looked up at
him questioningly.

Any discomfort that Travis may have been experiencing
had little to do with the cut on his lip. His eyes grew dark
and intent as he watched Cathy's wide-eyed concern.
"Why didn't he ever make love to you?" Travis asked
hoarsely in a deep, curious tone.

Cathy stared blankly at him for a long time, but the slight
color in her face was a clear indication that she'd heard
him and understood exactly Travis's point. "Wouldn't

you let him?" he added as that new thought occurred to him.

Cathy dropped her eyes to the two drops of blood on Travis's shirt. She twisted a wrist free from his hand and absently wiped at it with the bandanna. "Brian never asked," she said simply. "He's never been an outwardly demonstrative person." Cathy glanced briefly at Travis's dark face and light eyes, then back to his shirt. "Brian was always very sure of me, and sure of our—our relationship. He wasn't in any hurry...." She shrugged diffidently and also with a gnawing sense of embarrassment that perhaps he never found her attractive or sexy enough. "I suppose he was saving me for when we got married."

Travis's jaw tensed. "Do you want to marry him?" he asked roughly.

Without a moment's hesitation Cathy shook her head. "No! No, I don't. It—it just seemed that we would. Everyone always expected it...."

Cathy again touched the scarf to his mouth, and almost imperceptibly he winced.

"Did he hurt you?" she asked softly, her eyes misting with concern.

Travis searched her face with a thoughtful frown. She was a bit pale, and her eyes welled with tears, making the sable depths shimmer. Travis was still tense. "Were you afraid that he would?" he asked in a low, tight tone as he lifted a brow. "Or that I would hurt him?"

Cathy went stiff with the accusation, but he settled his arms around her, low on her back, and Cathy leaned back to stare at him. Their hips were pressed together, but she suddenly lifted her balled fists and lightly, in exasperation, hit him on his chest. "Travis! I didn't want to see either of you hurt! Don't forget you broke his wrist!"

He continued to scan her features. Very slowly, a complacent smile covered his mouth, and he slowly shook his head.

Cathy frowned and blinked at him. "What does that mean?" she asked in confusion.

A hand slid up her back along the spine, bringing the rest of her to lean into his body. Cathy relaxed her fists, uncurling them to hold on to his muscled arms. She let him bend to kiss her cheek, to nuzzle her neck and throat.

Travis's nose and corner of his mouth were sore, but he didn't care. She'd gotten no thrills over seeing two men fight over her. And she was still with him, not with Brian. Travis's arms tightened, feeling overwhelming, fierce possession for her.

"No, sweetheart, he could never hurt me," he murmured thickly into her soft skin.

Chapter Twelve

The entire episode was like a catalyst in their relationship. All the elements of their circumstances pulled and bunched, tumbled around together like a chemical formula. The final reaction, when it came, was explosive in two ways.

The first thing that happened was that Travis and Cathy were ultimately united emotionally. They made love that evening with a passion that bordered on desperation. It began with Cathy's stripping off Travis's bloodstained shirt with the intention of washing it at once. But Travis took the gesture more personally and also reached to remove her light camisole top. The mutual unrobing became serious and hurried until they faced each other naked. It was not as if they'd never seen each other naked before or had never come together intimately, but it was as if now the inherent implications of their nudity, each before the other, made them fully aware of the intimacy, the special and sacred meaning of their being together.

Travis looked at her carefully, his green eyes almost emerald, intense and bright with a light that Cathy should have recognized as love rather than mere physical need. For a long moment Travis reveled in the maturing of her body. The quality that had suggested adolescence when he'd first met her was gone. Her breasts were a little rounder and heavier. He knew that was the pregnancy. Though her stomach was still flat, the changes had added a curved softness to her hips. Cathy had been pretty before, appealing and young. Now she was totally desirable as a woman, and Travis wanted her badly.

But it was Cathy who took the initiative, again showing

how she'd changed since being with Travis. She was more alert to both his need and hers and no longer afraid or hesitant. She had discovered and amply explored her passionate nature with Travis, and it was only with him that she wanted to share it. She took hold of his hand and began urging him toward the bedroom.

"Love me." Her lips formed the words softly, and Travis was too overcome with pleasure and hope to respond verbally. But he needed no further prompting. He pulled his hand free, and lifting her off the floor against his chest, carried her to the room.

Travis never released her. He bent a knee to the edge of the bed, coming forward to place Cathy on the bedding and lying with her all in the same strong, fluid motion. His hands released her to explore her body with erotic, devastatingly sensual intent, eliciting little gasps and moans. His mouth found a ripe, swollen breast, and with his teeth, he gently worried a nipple until it was hard and Cathy squirmed against him. Travis molded his hand around her bottom and pulled her tightly against his aroused middle, gently and repeatedly, until Cathy was clutching and beside herself with the need for the final and complete possession.

Their joining had always been satisfying, had always left them limp and sated and warmly damp in each other's arms. But this was the first time their loving, the ritualistic universal dance, had brought them to the peak of fulfillment at the same time. The pure joy of it brought tears to Cathy's eyes and had Travis holding her tenderly and giving sweet little kisses to her mouth.

At first it was as though Travis wanted her to prove that Brian meant nothing to her anymore. But his fears were mostly unfounded. Brian would always mean something to Cathy, but not the way Travis imagined. It was not to be supposed that someone who thought of himself as undeserving of love would reason that out under the present emotional circumstances.

And Cathy, in her turn, having settled so much of her past with the confrontation with Brian, clung to Travis as if he might now be a lifeline to the future. Their physical joining was like absolution, finally clearing the way for both of them to be what they really wanted to be—loved by the other. But the declaration took place silently, though vigorously, even their sounds of pleasure held in check reverently, as if they might otherwise dispel the magic that surrounded them.

It was a new tenderness that extended itself around them and into the days that followed. It left them blind to important realities, even until Cathy's first trimester had passed.

The second thing happened so fast it would be weeks before the implications were fully understood and dealt with. It was the night Travis informed her he would have to return to Key West for an urgent consultation and the second of two nights in a row that Cathy hadn't eaten dinner. Travis's news had taken her by surprise, but since Cathy half convinced herself that Travis would have left sooner or later, anyway, she said nothing. She'd only nodded silently, her skin pale and finely drawn against what she was really feeling. Her easy and noncommittal acquiescence, however, did not sit well with Travis, who'd hoped that she would show some emotion at being separated from him.

Cathy's not eating had nothing to do with the news, though Travis suspected she thought he might be leaving for good. He could think of no way to convince her otherwise than to return as quickly as possible. But she was quiet and still and often vague in her response to him. By the second night Travis's patience with her was as fine as a razor's edge, but he was just as impatient with his inability to make things different for the moment. They could not go on this way, skirting an issue that affected so much of their lives.

On that second night Travis was sitting at the small dining table, looking over records and data of past hurricanes. His duffel was already packed by the front door. His dark brows were drawn together ominously in what seemed to be concentration laced with frustration. Cathy's continual withdrawal had not made things easier, and Travis now dreaded leaving her at all. The personal understanding they'd been on the verge of establishing seemed to be experiencing a considerable setback.

Travis drew on his cigarette deeply, the expelled smoke curling up mystically around his head. He looked up when Cathy walked quietly past him from her desk by the window to the kitchen. She had on a comfortable lilac-colored sundress with thin straps. Her curly hair had been pushed up in back and pinned there for coolness. Travis liked it that way, for it always reminded him of the White Rock girl in the beverage advertisements. He opened his mouth to ask her if she was all right, but she was gone before the words could be formed.

Cathy would not have heard him. She was listening to the sounds of her own body. It was telling her something important and imparting the information to her by way of slowly intensifying cramps. She couldn't remember if cold water had ever helped in the past, but getting up and walking around had to be better than sitting while her stomach twisted alarmingly. A fine sweat covered her forehead and chin. Waves of heat rushed up her neck and down again. Her hands shook around the glass. Something was wrong.

"Travis," Cathy breathed out in a thin whisper, impossible for him to hear. She kept her eyes on the kitchen doorway and tried to walk steadily in that direction. At the entrance she stopped and swayed against it. Her thighs felt numb. She wasn't sure she could stand much longer. Cathy's eyes looked to Travis, but he didn't seem to be in her line of vision. He seemed to have turned into vaporish gray clouds curling and swirling under a table light. "Travis..." Cathy tried again, the pain and panic finally instilled in the broken word. Then the glass slipped from her hands to the floor. The shattering sound echoed through her head, but her body sounds were louder. Cathy moaned, clutching her stomach, and her knees began to give way.

Travis lifted his head at the high-pitched utterance that was his name. The glass hit the floor and smashed, and he stared at her.

"Dammit, Cathy! Why can't you be more—" Travis was out of the chair. "Cathy! Oh, my God. Cathy!" Travis reached her before she touched the floor, his strong arms easily breaking her fall. Her head fell back limply, and she was doubled over in pain. "Cat...for heaven's sakes, what's wrong?" Travis asked anxiously, trying to lift her contorted body.

"Travis!" Cathy finally cried out, the name nearly lost in the forthcoming pain.

Travis lifted her and rushed with her to the bed, gently laying her down. Her knees remained tightly drawn up, her body stiff, her face pinched closed around what she was going through.

"Cathy," Travis called, his fear rising. But she was now beyond the ability to respond, reacting totally to the demands of her body, and at the moment it was demanding much.

Perspiration made her face shiny and feverish; her hands were clenched into such tight fists that her knuckles went stark white. She only loosened them enough to grab the bed linens and hold on. Travis's hand shook as he touched her cheek. She was ice cold despite the damp skin, her breathing deep and ragged with pain. Travis rushed to the phone and dialed the local emergency number.

"Nine-one-one. Emergency...can I help you?"

"Yes! I have an emergency here."

"What's the problem?" the cold, precise voice interrupted.

"The problem?" Travis repeated blankly. Cathy cried out again, and Travis looked toward the open bedroom door. "God, I don't know!" he bit out savagely into the phone. "She's in pain! She's doubled up and screaming in pain!"

"Could be an appendicitis attack," the operator offered, but Travis was shaking his head.

"No...no! Dammit, it's not that!"

"Okay, okay, buddy. Take it easy! Just give me the address and we'll send an ambulance."

Cathy cried out again, and then the sound was sharply cut off. The cords in Travis's neck stood out. The muscles in his arms were so tensed that his shirt was pulled tighter over his chest and shoulders. He was afraid she couldn't wait that long.

"No," he yelled. "Just call the hospital. *I'm* bringing her in!" And he slammed the phone down, oblivious of the fact he hadn't given his name or Cathy's.

Travis ran and pulled open the apartment door. Then he ran back to the room. His heart constricted and lurched painfully in his chest at the sight of her pain-racked body. Not attempting to separate Cathy from the bedspread she clung to, Travis hastily wrapped it around her and lifted his bundle carefully.

At the car, Travis struggled to get the car door opened, and half sat, half laid Cathy's blanket-wrapped body on the front seat. Getting behind the wheel of the small car, he screeched the car away from the curb and off down the street.

In just about any fair-sized city across the country, Friday and Saturday nights have been, traditionally by statistics, the nights of the most reported emergency cases. But it was Tuesday in Miami, and when Travis pulled to a stop at the emergency entrance of the county hospital, the driveway was completely clear of vehicles. The glass plate doors to the building automatically slid open, and a team of three women and one man, all dressed in hospital greens, rushed out with a collapsible gurney to the car.

Travis was once again lifting Cathy into his arms. Her head fell and rested on his shoulder. Her body jerked and tensed once with pain. Behind him Travis heard the emergency team approaching. For a fast private moment he pressed his lips to Cathy's brow.

"I love you," he whispered in a husky strangled voice, not wanting anything to happen to her before she knew that. "Do you hear me, Cat? I love you."

And then he was being helped to stretch her on the cot. The young resident taking charge began removing the blanket, letting the ends hang over the edge of the gurney. Travis's eyes blazed when he saw Cathy was now lying in a small circle of her own blood.

"God…" Travis said in anguish, afraid to even think what this meant. He grabbed her hand and held it tightly, her head turning in his direction, but her gaze was blind and wavering, and she couldn't focus on his, though she tried to say his name.

"We'll take it from here," the resident said, stepping briskly between Travis and his hold on Cathy's convulsively clutching hand. Travis was forced to let go.

"I'm coming with her!" he stated bluntly.

The resident, a thin, earnest young man behind wire-rimmed glasses, turned back to Travis and looked at him carefully. His quick professional eyes took in the hard, uncompromising line of the mouth, the strong jutting chin, but also the haggard concern and fright of the gray-green eyes. "Are you family? Her husband?" he asked quickly.

The muscles in Travis's jaw jumped abruptly to life. "No, dammit!" he said shortly through clenched teeth. The color stealing up his neck turned his face almost a dusty rose.

The resident understood, but slowly he shook his head. "Then I'm sorry, but you'll have to wait down here." He didn't wait for a response or further discussion but began shouting orders as the carrier bearing Cathy was rushed away. Travis didn't offer further words, as he realized that the most important thing was getting Cathy some medical help. He watched helplessly as they took her away. In frustration he balled a fist and struck it violently against the nearest wall, cursing through his clenched teeth. A hospital aide, passing near him with a tray of bottles and vials, jumped, and a number of items fell on their sides, rolling around the metal surface.

But Travis never noticed him, or anything else. He was suddenly caught in the nightmare of watching his brother trapped in a burning plane, screaming for him to help. Travis leaned back against the wall, his images holding him rigid, his guilt and agony tearing away at him. But then Travis forced himself straight and with both hands swept the fingers through his hair.

"No more..." he gritted out softly to himself. "No more!"

Mitch was dead, It was over. It was forever and would never change. Travis's questions were useless, because they would never be answered. He was the only one who wondered if Mitch forgave him, the only one who could judge his guilt—and it no longer mattered. What mattered was Cathy, because she was real. She was here and now, and he loved her. Had she heard him? Why hadn't he told her before? Why was he always waiting until it was too late to say, "I'm sorry," and "I love you"?

Travis paced the hall in front of the closed surgical door, not even able to hear sounds from within. And his own imagination conjured up enough horrors she might be going through to justify the look of sheer fright that now held him prisoner. He could only think that she might miscarry the baby. He could only believe that it was all his fault.

His mind cleared momentarily as Travis tried to think what to do. Gratefully, he remembered the name Elizabeth Harris, the woman at the health center whom Cathy had spoken so often of with such high regard. Jolting himself out of his shock, Travis walked down the hospital corridor until he located a nurses' station. The lone woman seated turned a lazy eye to him when he began talking.

"Look, I'd appreciate it if you could call someone for me. Her name is Elizabeth Harris, and she's with the—the Women's Health Center, or the Alternative Center—something like that!" Travis finished, impatient that he couldn't remember exactly which it was.

The nurse at the station looked at the man before her, seeing the same thing the young resident had. But her expression was unsympathetic and bland, and she began to shake her head. "I'm sorry, sir, but I'm not supposed to do that. There are public tele—"

"This is an emergency!" Travis said tightly, trying to keep a reign on his desire to just reach over the counter and use the phone to dial himself, without her permission.

"Yes, I understand that, sir, but the rules are—"

"I don't give a damn about your rules!" Travis bit out angrily. "I can't leave her right now. I have to stay here in case—" Travis clamped his mouth closed. In case of what? He didn't know.

The nurse didn't, either, and experience had taught her not to care too much. Everyone had a story, and she'd seen more tragedies than she cared to remember. But this man—this was a strong man faced with a situation out of his control. He would never ask for help easily. And though he did now, she sensed it was not for himself. She sighed.

"Well, since I'm alone for the moment, I don't suppose it'll matter too much," she said, still very much in control of herself. "What did you say the name was again?"

Elizabeth Harris was not at the center, but since a nurse was calling her from the country hospital, her home phone number was given. As the nurse began dialing a second time, she looked evenly at Travis.

"This is the last one, mister. If she's not there, you'll have to use the public phones and try on your own."

Fortunately, Elizabeth was home and surprised when Travis introduced himself. Elizabeth knew at once who he was. Deep concern then took over her surprise.

"Is something wrong with Cathy?" Elizabeth asked without preamble.

"I brought her in fifteen minutes ago. I—I don't know what's wrong, and they wouldn't let me go with her," Travis said bitterly. Then he stopped and let out a deep breath, calming himself. "Mrs. Harris, I have to be with her," Travis said in a low broken voice. "I belong with her."

"Yes, of course you do," Elizabeth readily agreed. "Don't worry. I'll be there in twenty minutes," she said, and she quickly hung up.

Elizabeth Harris's agreeing to come to the hospital did not lessen Travis's anxiety one bit. But now he at least felt there was someone who might understand and appreciate his position. Uttering a vague and tired thanks to the nurse, Travis went back to his vigil by the examining-room door where they'd taken Cathy. The normal pace of hospital routine went on around him, and Travis was suddenly, irrationally, angry that no one seemed to care about Cathy's emergency. No more personnel came hurrying to her crisis, and his. Didn't they know that nothing could happen to her now? She was the most important thing in the world to him.

Travis groaned and fingered his hair. *This is what I do to people,* he thought remorsefully. He destroyed the ones he most loved and walked away from the ones he most needed. He left a path of destruction and broken lives wherever he went, and all the irresponsibility his father had always accused him of seemed absolutely true. He thought he was safe from the world, and the world from him, on the houseboat in Key West. The boat that had belonged to Mitchell and Melinda and the boys for their vacation until Cathy had wandered into his life and shown him how lonely and limited that life had been. With her romantic nonsense and fantasy beliefs, her cockeyed optimism and wishful thinking. He didn't deserve someone like her. He didn't rate her youth and hope or joy. And if she would just pull out of this, he'd let her go.

THE HOSPITAL WAS DEADLY QUIET, Travis thought grimly. At four thirty-seven in the morning, the only sounds were the occasional squeaky heels of rubber-soled shoes on tile floors or the faint rattling of bottles as prescribed medicine was given to patients. It was all background noise to Travis, who leaned wearily against a wall, his eyes staring blankly into space, a lit but unsmoked cigarette in his fingers. Some sixth sense told him the kindled end had burned its way down almost to his skin, and with a movement that demonstrated total physical and emotional exhaustion, he walked to flick the butt into a trash bin.

"Travis?" came the sound of his name. He looked quickly over his shoulder and saw Elizabeth Harris standing with two cups of coffee in her hands. Travis straightened, and keeping his eyes on the features of the middle-aged black woman, he walked slowly toward her.

Elizabeth smiled kindly at him, and at once Travis relaxed, sensing that nothing further was amiss. She extended one cup to him. "Here, I think you'd better drink this, or you're likely to be the next emergency!" Elizabeth said softly.

Travis ruefully lifted a corner of his mouth in a half smile and accepted the cup. "Thanks, Mrs. Harris."

"Elizabeth," she corrected easily. She took a small sip from her cup and over the rim eyed the tall man before her.

"Is, ah, is she going to be all right?" Travis asked with deceptive calm, but Elizabeth noticed that his hands fairly gripped the Styrofoam cup.

"Cathy will be fine, but I'm not so sure about you!" Elizabeth said pointedly. "I've talked to the doctors."

Travis's head came up sharply; his five-o'clock shadow and bleary eyes made him look almost derelict.

"They'll permit you to stay with her now, since she has no family here in Florida." Travis bit back the words, *I'm her family!* "And she's clearly not in any danger."

He nodded and then frowned at her. "Did—did they say—"

Elizabeth raised a tired brow and chuckled dryly. "Actually, they said quite a lot. Let's go sit down somewhere and talk."

Travis followed the thin woman to another section of the corridor that had comfortable chairs and tables placed around a small alcove. They both sat quietly for a while drinking their coffee.

"I suppose you know Cathy lost the baby," Elizabeth said in a soft voice without looking at Travis directly.

His jaw clenched tightly. He nodded silently, staring into the coffee cup.

Elizabeth sighed, rubbing a tired eye with the heel of her hand. "Actually, she didn't lose it. They had to abort, Travis. She was in trouble, and there really wasn't a choice."

"What happened?" he asked tonelessly.

"Well, it was a tear in her cervix—it was that that created all the cramping pain. And of course she began to hemorrhage quickly. She lost a lot of blood. On top of that, oxygen was cut off to the fetus. The most important thing, however, was stemming the flow of blood before Cathy went into shock." Elizabeth turned worried eyes to the man next to her. "Do you understand, Travis? Her life came first. And the baby had already lacked so much oxygen—"

"I understand," he whispered hoarsely. Elizabeth could see the hesitation in him and waited patiently, her head tilted to the side. Travis tensed his jaw and swept a hand through his already-disordered hair. "Look, I—I made love to her the night before and..." He paused as his awkwardness made it hard to go on.

"Yes?" Elizabeth prompted quietly. Travis turned questioning, cloudy eyes to the woman.

"Did I do something to hurt her?" The voice was deeply pained.

It took a few seconds for his meaning to make itself clear to Elizabeth. She began to shake her head strongly. "No," she reassured Travis, "it's highly unlikely—"

"But not impossible!" Travis countered shortly.

Elizabeth searched his face and saw the doubt and self-derisive accusation in his eyes. "That's certainly true," she conceded, "but I don't believe you did anything to cause what happened last night. That's been happening a long time. And I recall telling Cathy that if she proceeded with the pregnancy, there might be problems."

Travis nodded and took another deep gulp of the coffee. Satisfied that he was alert, Elizabeth sat back wearily in her chair. "Did you know Cathy never expected to ever have children? Did she tell you about herself?"

"No, she didn't, but I found out. I read the paper she submitted to you. It was very telling." Travis said hoarsely.

"Then you have some idea how terribly confusing and difficult it's been for her. She had a difficult decision to make," Elizabeth said carefully, not knowing to what extent Travis was now involved in Cathy's life and only concerned that Cathy's position be clearly stated and understood.

Travis looked at Elizabeth, his tired sea-green eyes probing her dark brown ones. "Did she tell you she wanted an abortion?"

Elizabeth returned his look, and letting out a sigh, gestured with a long, narrow hand helplessly. "I told her at the beginning it was something to think about. But Cathy didn't ever consider it seriously. She never made any attempts to arrange for one."

Travis averted his eyes momentarily and pursed his lips caustically. "That was probably my fault. I pressured her into waiting."

Elizabeth was surprised, but she only sighed and shook her head. "I don't think she was ever really sure what to do. And now it doesn't matter."

Travis wanted to refute that. He wanted to tell Elizabeth that now it mattered more than ever. But he wanted to tell Cathy first.

Elizabeth could see Travis didn't fully agree with her last statement, and she sat up straight again. "Travis, Cathy wanted the baby. *Your* baby," she qualified because she sensed that would be important to him. "She just wasn't sure she knew how to be a good mother. She was feeling very young, inexperienced and unprepared, and to some extent it's true," Elizabeth said softly and in sympathy.

Travis finished his coffee in one last gulp, the ensuing silence allowing him to deal with Cathy's loss and his own privately. He turned again to Elizabeth. "Was this just a fluke, or can she conceive again?"

Elizabeth relaxed and shrugged. "The doctors don't see that there's any reason why she couldn't. They do suggest that she wait a while, maybe a year or more, and if she did become pregnant, she should be closely supervised by her doctor. What happened to her last night needn't happen again." Elizabeth wondered if Travis's interest in Cathy extended into the future or if it ended here and now along with the pregnancy. "I, er, I don't mean to pry, but did you want her to have an abortion?"

Travis almost smiled at Elizabeth. "You're hardly prying. I know you're interested in Cathy's welfare." Travis sighed and absently reached for his crushed pack of cigarettes. "I would have preferred her not to have the abortion," he said, shaking one cigarette from the pack and lighting it. "But if I believed she really wanted one, I wouldn't have stopped her," he ended bleakly, staring moodily at the burning end. "I understand that under the circumstances I—I had no say in what she did." Travis's voice was tight and hard, and both he and Elizabeth were thinking the same thing. That his tie to Cathy was tenuous at best.

Elizabeth sipped at her coffee. "What do you want to do

now?'' she asked softly, with curiosity, feeling for this man and for Cathy.

Travis drew on the cigarette and tilted his head back against the wall and stared up at the ceiling. "I want to stay with her," he answered simply. "But I can't. At least not yet." Travis turned to face Elizabeth's frowning silent inquiry. "I work for the hurricane center, but I fly out of Key West. There's evidence that some small tropical turbulence in the Atantic Ocean and western Caribbean could develop into major storms within the next few weeks. I have to do some fact checking for the weather bureau in preparation. I have to leave Miami for at least two days...maybe more."

Elizabeth's eyes softened in understanding. "And then what happens?" she asked further.

Travis thought for a long moment, putting out the cigarette in the empty Styrofoam cup. "Then we try to start over." He looked with bright but tired anxiety-filled eyes at Elizabeth. "If she'll have me."

IT WAS NEARLY NOON that day when Cathy slowly dragged open her eyelids, only to have them close again. They were unbelievably heavy, but she felt the need not to succumb again to that dark pain and drug-induced world of suspended animation. She pulled the lids open once more. There was a strange grid over her head of lines and dots and fluorescent lighting fixtures. The air smelled pugently sterile. It was very quiet, although there seemed to be muted sounds of movement and words beyond a door somewhere.

Something was holding tightly to her hand. Her fingers felt numb, her arm stiff, and she tried to move them. At once the hold on her hand tightened. Trying to swallow from a dry and dusty-feeling throat, Cathy rolled her head to the side. Her vision began to blur, the images fuzzy and swaying. There was a tube in her arm, and beyond it she blinked drowsily at Travis's face. He slowly came into focus. He seemed extraordinarily tired and grim, his eyes bloodshot and rimmed with red. With tremendous effort Cathy blinked and fought to stay awake.

Travis tried giving her an easy smile at finding her awake. He leaned on the edge of the bed and reached out with the back of his hand to stroke gently down her pale cool cheek. "Hello, sleepyhead," his whispered in a husky voice.

Cathy wanted to answer. She wanted to return his smile and the pressure to his fingers, but the only things that moved were her eyelids, and even those did so with heavy reluctance. Cathy tried to move her mouth, but nothing came out. And then she was aware of something else. She felt sore—a low-level throbbing of pain in her stomach. She had an overwhelming urge to move a hand and touch her stomach, but she couldn't move to do that, either, and she knew instinctively she didn't have to. With obvious difficulty Cathy tried swallowing again. Travis got up at once and reached for the water carafe on her bedside stand. But already she was forcing slow, croaking words through her dry lips.

"I...I lost...the baby..." she said with insight in an almost inaudible tone. Travis froze in place next to her. Cathy dragged her eyes to him, and in that instant his expression said everything. "The baby...baby is gone," she moaned weakly, half in delirium and half in genuine agitation that Travis couldn't interpret.

"Cathy?" he said, leaning over her. But her eyes were closed again, and she was once more asleep. Travis stared at her for a long time and with his large hand gently pushed the curly hair from her forehead. He took a finger and with a feather-light touch ran it along her jaw to her chin, watching her face, at the moment serene and peaceful and free of pain. There hadn't even been enough time for him to repeat that he loved her. And the quicker he left, the quicker he could return. Eizabeth said the doctors wanted to keep Cathy for another two days at least. And if he hurried...

Travis slowly bent forward and touched his lips tenderly to Cathy's. "I love you," he whispered against the coolness of her skin. "I love you, sweetheart, and I'll be back for you. I promise."

Chapter Thirteen

Cathy slipped her feet into the high-heeled summer sandals and then stood straight to adjust her slim white skirt and the silky capped-sleeve blouse tucked into its band. Her mind was preoccupied, and she paid little attention to the fact that the band of the skirt was decidedly loose, denoting a loss of weight, or that the same weight loss clearly showed the shape of her face with its square jaw. Her neck seemed longer, her mouth fuller and curved. The slight youthful softness was gone from all over her body, replaced by a slender womanliness that was becoming and attractive. But that, too, went unnoticed.

Automatically, Cathy packed the rest of her things into the suitcase laid open on the bed and took a brief look around to make sure she had all she needed. The bedroom seemed strange. For that matter, so did the whole apartment. It was unbelievably quiet and empty and lonely. And one night there by herself after being brought home from the hospital by Eizabeth Harris was enough to make Cathy want to leave it again and go somewhere familiar and warm. So Cathy was packing to go home to Baltimore. At least for a while.

She wasn't capable of making any decisions beyond that, and that one had been difficult enough. Cathy had no idea what she'd say to Chad about her precipitous return, and she wasn't going to worry about it now. She simply had to go. She had to get away from Florida, Miami, the apartment and the painful and overwhelming thoughts of Travis. At least to her it had seemed painful. But Cathy was willing to concede the point that her recent trauma and subsequent recovery time might be affecting her perception. Whatever—he was gone, and she was alone.

Cathy put the suitcase by the door and checked to make sure most of the windows were closed and secured. She put the plastic cover over her typewriter and checked to make sure she had her notes, manuscripts and ideas to take with her, although she wasn't sure she'd really be able to get any writing done at all. She noticed Travis's brown suede jacket over the back of one of the dining-room chairs. For a second hope sprang alive within her, because since he had left his jacket it might mean that he would still return. But Cathy quickly squelched the hope. She had to, because he might not ever return. Why should he, now that the problem of the baby was resolved?

Sudden waves of depression snaked their way through her mind, and her eyes filled with tears. She smoothed a hand lovingly over the soft fabric and turned away. She wasn't going to cry again. She'd done that all the night before until she was too tired to bring forth another tear. And she'd done it the whole afternoon after she'd come to in the hospital, only to find Elizabeth Harris waiting patiently for her to regain consciousness—and Travis already gone.

When Cathy came to the second time, it was almost five o'clock. The shade had been lowered against the late-afternoon sun, but the light sneaking in nonetheless was orange and warm and infused the room with a mellow glow. Her door was partially open, and she stared dumbly at the space until, as if by magic, a nurse appeared and cheerfully proceeded to admonish Cathy for sleeping the whole day away. She also added that everyone was concerned and that she must be positively starved. All the words slid off Cathy's consciousness like water off a duck's back.

Cathy was positive that she'd awakened before and that Travis had been sitting right next to her, tightly holding her hand. She even thought she recalled his having whispered wonderful words to her like "I love you." Cathy turned her head to follow the busy, efficient movements of the nurse, who still expounded on something or other about getting better and cheering up. Cathy was about to ask her if anyone was outside waiting to see her when the nurse turned to her.

"Oh, by the way, there's someone waiting to see you now—the whole night as a matter of fact!" She came to check Cathy's water carafe and the tube feeding into her arm and to quickly take her pulse and temperature. "Do you feel up to a visitor?" the nurse asked, her eyes squinting to read the modern digital thermometer.

Cathy slowly nodded, even though she was feeling weak and still very tired. The anticipation was making her heart race. The nurse replaced the thermometer in its self-sterilizing mount and moved to the door.

"Okay, you can have about fifteen minutes. Then the doctor wants to see you before he goes off duty. And I'm sure you'd like something else to eat besides liquids dripping into your arm!"

When Eizabeth Harris walked into the room and quietly closed the door, it was all Cathy could do to give her a smile. She wasn't unhappy to see Elizabeth. She was just hoping desperately for her visitor to be Travis. Elizabeth was perfectly aware of the instantaneous light sparking and then dying in Cathy's eyes. She was not at all personally offended. She understood very well the dynamics of the situation and had nothing but sympathy for the younger woman, looking so small and pale under the white hospital bed linens. Elizabeth spoke first, which was just as well, since Cathy had an enormous lump of emotion wedged in her throat.

"Hello, Cathy. How are you feeling?"

"Weak...and awfully tired."

"That's pretty normal for what you've been through." Elizabeth pulled the one chair in the room closer to the bed and sat down facing Cathy. Cathy's hands lay motionless across her stomach, but Elizabeth couldn't immediately determine what Cathy was feeling about what had taken place.

"How...long have you been waiting?" Cathy asked quietly, her eyes on her hands.

"Since about seven o'clock last night."

Cathy's eyes widened in surprise. "Oh, Elizabeth! I—I am sorry!"

Elizabeth patted her arm comfortingly. "No need to be sorry. I'm glad I was called."

Cathy frowned. "Who called you?"

Elizabeth watched Cathy's face carefully. "Travis—just after he got you here. I came right over."

At the mention of his name, Cathy swallowed and averted her eyes. She wasn't going to ask; she wasn't going to seem desperate. But she simply couldn't fool Elizabeth. Besides, in her present state, Cathy's wan face easily revealed her emotions.

"It wasn't so bad," Elizabeth said lightly. "Travis and I kept each other company and shared about three gallons of coffee!" Cathy's expression brightened perceptively. "And we got to know each other. I arranged with the doctor for him to stay with you."

"Stay with me?" Cathy mouthed.

Elizabeth nodded. She furrowed her brows briefly and shrugged a shoulder. "They weren't going to let him stay since—since he wasn't immediate family. I persuaded them otherwise."

A kind of horrified look came into Cathy's enormous dark eyes as the implications became clear to her. Color flooded her face and quickly drained out again. She couldn't open her mouth. She was paralyzed to say what was on her mind.

Elizabeth could see what Cathy was going through. She smiled gently. "He was here with you, Cathy. Once the doctors were finished and brought you to your room, Travis was by your side all night—and very worried about you."

"What happened?" Cathy asked, her voice quavering.

For a quick moment Elizabeth was stumped. She didn't know if Cathy referred to Travis or the baby. She considered for a moment and decided it was best to cover the latter. They'd get back to Travis in a moment. Carefully, she outlined what had happened and what had been done to prevent further complications medically. Cathy listened quietly, her fingers plucking and picking nervously on the bed linens, her dark looping curls partially hiding her eyes and face as her head bent forward slightly. She made not a sound, but Elizabeth noted two teardrops making spots on the sheets and the back of Cathy's hand. Elizabeth reached out and took one of the hands into her own.

"Cathy, you can have other children—when you're ready. It's possible now, you know."

Cathy shook her head vigorously, her shoulders slumped and rounded with her pain. "I won't! There won't ever be a chance!" she murmured brokenly, and only she knew she was referring to Travis and the hopes she'd harbored of having a life with him.

"Yes, there will! You just need time to get better now and put this behind you." And it occurred to Eizabeth that there was much more on Cathy's mind. "Travis said he would be back, Cathy," Elizabeth said, and that was all. She had no right to add her interpretation of Travis's feelings toward Cathy. She believed that he might truly love her, but Cathy would have to learn that for herself. Just as Travis would have to find out alone that Cathy indeed loved him, too.

"He won't!" Cathy said with sad, fatalistic insight. "He doesn't have to anymore. His obligation to me is over!"

"Perhaps," Elizabeth said uncomfortably. "But he didn't want to leave you like this."

"Then why did he leave?" Cathy asked tightly.

"He said because of his job in Key West. He said it would only be a few days."

But Cathy continued to shake her head, and finally, as if unable to hold it up anymore, she let it drop back against her pillows, her eyes closed. "He won't," she repeated softly, with conviction. There was nothing more Elizabeth could say to convince Cathy otherwise. She only hoped she hadn't been wrong about Travis and that he was sincere. The door opened, and the nurse bounced in again.

"Sorry, ladies. I'll have to call a halt to your visit. The doctor is waiting to see the patient."

Elizabeth stood up and gathered her purse and jacket, reluctant nonetheless to leave Cathy alone with her despondency. When she squeezed Cathy's hand in farewell,

Cathy suddenly grabbed at the hand frantically. Elizabeth frowned with concern into Cathy's tear-stained face.

"Elizabeth! I want to go home. Please! When can I go home?"

The nurse appeared not to have heard the question as she fastened the door open and quietly left again with the final warning to Elizabeth. "Two minutes, please."

Elizabeth nodded and turned back to Cathy. "I think they may want you to stay until Friday, Cathy. And I believe the doctor wants to give you a prescription for birth-control pills."

"Okay," Cathy said numbly, still holding to Elizabeth's hand. "But I still want to go home!" she added strongly. Cathy couldn't explain to Elizabeth that now she felt bereft and alien to everything around her. She had nothing around her that was familiar and comforting, that made her feel safe and less disoriented. Cathy only recognized that she'd been through a painful experience and that essentially she was now alone. Except for Elizabeth. Thank heavens at least Elizabeth was there. The tears began to fall in earnest as she thought of Travis. She wanted him. She wanted to have him come through the door right now and dispel the awful dark cloud descending upon her. But Travis wasn't there, so she wanted to go home.

"I'll mention it to the doctor if you like. But you really should wait." Elizabeth was also hoping to gain time for Travis so that he could return as he'd said he wanted to.

Elizabeth soon left, and Cathy gave free reign to her despair. And the doctor, finding her thus, tried to tell her she could have other babies, obviously not aware of the full extent of his patient's concerns. Cathy couldn't eat dinner and only lay sadly in her bed, thinking how her life had plummeted through the past three months. April had promised so much, and now, nearly the end of July, it would seem that she had hit absolute rock bottom.

CATHY CAME OUT of her reverie to find that she was sitting on the love seat, absently turning the pages of her frayed copy of *The Little Prince*. Almost impatiently, Cathy put it aside and stood up. She checked her watch, knowing her cab should be arriving any moment now. She'd turned in her leased car to the agency, not sure how long she was going to be away from Miami or even if she would ever return. She had never been absolutely sure she liked Miami, but she would forever connect it with Travis and the baby and the period when she came of age.

With a frantic urgency Cathy knew that this was the right decision. She had to see her brother and be home again. She was a different person going back to Baltimore from the one who'd left there. Perhaps not so much different as just having learned so much more. Her future might hold more possibilities than before. Her life could go in many more directions. She had learned about the full extent of being a person—and a woman. She had learned about fears and sacrifices, wanting and needing, giving and loss. She had learned much about the different faces of love. Travis had taught her that in those few short weeks of uncertainty together. In his own way, under the circumstances, maybe he did love her. That she wanted, ultimately, to know the full knowledge of his love and would never have it was her own unique cross to bear. The same way she had to deal with having been unexpectedly pregnant and then having lost the child.

Cathy felt so empty and, to a degree, so lacking in the ability to function as a woman. She only knew that something had existed between her and Travis. Something unique had been lost, but also something had been gained. The little girl was gone, the woman emerging from pain and experience, trial and tribulation—her wonder, curiosity and hope no less important to her but now placed differently. She still had to get on with the business of living, and a tremendous part of that had been growing up—at last.

TRAVIS HAD BEEN in a near rage to find his calls couldn't be put through to Cathy. There was no phone in her room. To make matters more frustrating, the operator would only give him the most general report on her condition. The patient was in satisfactory condition, and she was responding to treatment. It was what he wasn't being told that was driving Travis crazy. Did Cathy understand that he'd had to leave her? Did she realize that he had every intention of coming back to her and starting a real relationship? Did she know how much he loved her and how it was tearing him apart not to be there?

The final insult had been when the operator even refused to forward a message. They weren't allowed to do that. In bitter anger Travis had slammed the phone down, cutting off the indifferent apology. That had been Wednesday evening. All day Thursday Travis was in the air. The one time he'd landed to refuel, the switchboard lines had been busy. Finally, as a last resort, he called Elizabeth Harris, who told him that Cathy was doing well but was predictably depressed and a little withdrawn.

Travis violently and helplessly cursed the bad timing that had taken him so far away from her. But when Elizabeth told him she was to be released on Friday, Travis knew near defeat that had not even been paralleled by the death of his brother. *That*, he recognized now, he couldn't have done anything about. His situation with Cathy could be remedied and saved if he was in Miami with her.

Elizabeth didn't tell him that Cathy had talked of going home to Baltimore, because she wasn't absolutely sure that it was Cathy's intention. And there was always the hope that Travis would get back to Cathy before she could get herself organized and out of Florida. In the end, they both underestimated Cathy's need and determination.

Travis may have been unreliable in his father's eyes and quick to act before thinking things out, but he'd never been that way with job responsibilities. For the first time in his life he gave emotional thought to resigning a responsibility because he really wanted to be somewhere else. But the panic of that desire was fleeting, and when he'd calmed down, he knew that events would have to follow a prescribed course of action over which he had no control. But it was galling, and it took its toll on him. By Friday night he was like a zombie, totally worn out both physically and emotionally.

Travis got back to his base on Key West utterly exhausted and slept most of Saturday away. He could only think to get back to Miami now. His heart was more than willing, but he simply didn't have the strength. On Saturday he called the hospital to hear what he'd half expected—that Catherine Donnelly had been released two days before. When he called the apartment and got a recording that said the line had been temporarily disconnected, Travis knew she was no longer in Miami. Travis knew the temptation to go out and get stoned drunk, but the idea grew quickly unappealing, and in self-derisive disgust he knew that wasn't going to ease his pain or anxiety. But all at once he knew what would.

He, too, needed to go home. He wanted to see his father. He wanted to make peace with him. He wanted to apologize for all the unnecessary hurt, misunderstandings, misplaced pride—and lost time. He wanted a chance to say that maybe he couldn't be the kind of son his father wanted, but he'd be there when he was needed. With that decision came another for Travis. He wanted to meet with Chad Donnelly and explain how he and Cathy met and what had happened between them. If Cathy had gone back to Baltimore, and Travis believed now she had, then she shouldn't have to explain and possibly endure condemnation all alone. And he had no intention of letting anyone make her feel ashamed of what they'd been to each other.

The emergency call for him in Key West had been real. There was a strong likelihood that a hurricane was developing off the coast of Florida and would come to full force by mid-September. He didn't have much time for what he wanted to do and accomplish both in Baltimore and Boston, and he'd have to come back quickly to Key West—with or without Cathy.

CHAD WALKED SLOWLY down the airport corridor, mindful of people, children, luggage and skycaps crossing his path. However, his eyes were trained easily over most people's heads as he searched out one in particular. Chad spotted at once the airport tavern and restaurant, unimaginatively called the Cockpit, and began making his way to the entrance. A quick glance at his watch showed that he was only about five minutes late. But as he looked up, he saw Travis approaching him from the opposite corridor.

The two men quickly searched over each other for a second time, the present circumstances much different from the first but the reasons for meeting the same—Cathy.

Chad's original impressions of Travis were reinforced. A strong, fit man, a little weary and unhappy-looking around the eyes and mouth, but with the obvious physical appeal to attract women. On his own instincts Chad also judged him to be honest and straightforward, intelligent and not afraid of very much. Whatever might have any kind of power over him was likely to be something abstract. Travis was dressed comfortably for traveling in gray slacks and a forest-green velour top.

For his part Travis was again struck by the similarities between brother and sister. The same dark brown eyes and curly hair, although Chad's was lighter in color. The same square jaw. But whereas Cathy's face had always expressed open curiosity and trust, Chad's was wearily curious—and cautious.

The two men met, searched each other's eyes and intent and, relaxing only slightly, shook hands silently. Chad held the door, and Travis preceded him into the dimly lit tavern. All of the tables were in use, and Travis automatically went to the very end of the bar and settled on the last stool, Chad settling next to him. The silence was decidedly awkward, and understandable. They each gave orders for beer, and Travis went through the ritual of lighting a cigarette. Chad spoke first.

"What time is your connecting flight?" he asked, using his fingertip to twirl the cardboard coaster on the counter in front of him.

Travis turned over his wrist, reading his watch. "I have two hours," he answered. The two men again caught each other's eye. Travis raised a quizzical brow at the amusement in Chad's face.

"I have to tell you—" Chad began. "Coming down that

corridor, you looked like you expected me to meet you with three or four of my buddies to work you over!"

Travis chuckled dryly, exhaling from his cigarette. "Something like that. Let's say I was at least prepared for your wrath."

Chad was curious. "Why?" he asked.

Travis turned a surprised expression to Chad, who was waiting honestly for an answer. Travis sidestepped the issue by asking his own question. "How's Cathy?"

Chad dropped his eyes to his beer and pursed his lips. "She's okay. A little pale. A little thin. Very tired. She hasn't told me why she's back in Baltimore, and I haven't asked. It's still her home, and she can return anytime she wants. When she has something to say, she'll say it." He lifted his beer and drank from it.

Travis frowned. "Aren't you the least bit curious?" he asked in disbelief.

Chad gave him a wry grin. "The suspense is killing me! But whatever has happened to Cathy—or between you two—is none of my business." He turned sobering eyes to Travis. "I just don't want to see her hurt...that's all."

The remark only made Travis frown. He'd every intention of telling Chad that Cathy had been pregnant but had to have a therapeutic abortion, anyway. But he knew now he couldn't do that. The pregnancy was just between himself and Cathy, and telling Chad would not solve his immediate problem—communicating with Cathy. Travis took another sip of the beer. "Well, if it makes you feel any better, my intentions toward her are only the best."

Chad looked thoughtfully at him for a long moment and nodded. "I know that. You wouldn't be here otherwise." He played with the coaster again. "Let me ask you this. Why aren't you talking directly to Cathy?"

Travis puffed on his cigarette. It was a perfectly reasonable question to which he had no answer. "We, er, we had differing opinions on something. I had to leave Miami on business before we cleared it up. By the time I got back, she was already gone."

Chad digested that, sipping his bear and thoughtfully

examining the fast-disappearing head on the brew. "Now that I think about it, I'm not sure it would have done you much good to talk to her."

Travis went cold inside and felt a distinct chill of apprehension stiffen the hairs on the back of his neck. "Why do you say that?" he asked with more calm than he felt.

The coaster was spun around again. Chad shrugged. "She said she didn't want to talk to anyone. She's only been home four days, and even *I* haven't really spoken to her."

Chad could not have know that Cathy's announcement did not extend to Travis, but since even Cathy hadn't expected Travis to try to reach her, she hadn't thought to mention as much to her brother. And Chad, now repeating her orders, was of the personal opinion that if it would save his sister from being further upset and give her time to regain her color along with her spirit, then perhaps it was a good thing.

Impatiently, Travis stubbed out the cigarette in the ashtray. "I'm on my way to Boston to see my—my family. I—I thought I'd stop by and see—I just wanted to say—"

"Yeah, I know," Chad interpreted easily, and Travis gave him a grateful glance. Travis ordered a second round of beers.

"So what do you think of my baby sister?" Chad asked conversationally.

The question made Travis tense his jaw. Again he was thinking that what he thought or felt for Cathy was still personal and somewhat classified. But he turned truthfully to Chad. "I think quite a lot of her," he said almost to himself. "I've never met anyone like her," he added simply and honestly. "I've never met anyone who gets such a kick out of life! Everything surprises her. She's like a wide-eyed kid turned loose in a toy shop. A sunny day makes her smile," Travis whispered in renewed wonder, and the memory of her excitement only sent a fresh stab of love for her shooting through his chest.

"Well, that certainly was true," Chad agreed.

Travis's head came up sharply. "Was?" he asked Chad evenly.

"Something's changed. I would say...that wide-eyed little girl is growing up. She's not the same innocent she was when she decided to leave Baltimore. I can see she's been through some changes. Maybe it's a good thing. It's too late now, but I should have been more the big brother for her. You know what I mean? Someone she could really talk to. Instead, she got left behind at home with Dad, who taught her to be a great dreamer but not how to always keep her eyes open!"

Travis fingered his hair restlessly. "I have to see her, Chad."

Chad look at him. "Yeah, I can see that you do. But you want to know what I think? Give her some time. If you two care for each other, then that's not going to change. But Cathy needs some time. My guess is when the smoke clears, you're the first person she'll want to see."

Travis wasn't sure Chad was right. More had happened to Cathy than he obviously knew, and Travis wasn't so sure Cathy would ever want to see him again. Maybe she did need some time to herself. He only hoped that he hadn't lost her for good. They say absence makes the heart grow fonder, but Travis's own experience had been that the heart often forgets.

Chad watched with both understanding and amusement the tense anxiety of Travis's face. "You've got it bad, don't you?" he commented.

"Does it show that much?" Travis asked with caustic humor.

"About as much as it shows on Cathy," Chad confided quietly. When Travis realized what he'd said, he relaxed notably and finished his second beer. Maybe there was hope, after all.

"I wanted to ask you something," Travis said thoughtfully now. "Cathy seems to be terrified of violent thunderstorms. That's not so unusual, but in her case, do you know why?"

Chad nearly choked on his beer and shot Travis an almost sheepish look. "Yeah, I think I know why. One summer when I was about fourteen, Brian and I were playing in a softball league. Cathy was about six then, and my Dad used to make me take her along to the games. But there was nothing for her to do, and she used to go wandering off, playing games by herself. It sometimes took Brian and me an hour afterward to find her.

"Then one day Brian got the bright idea to take her to an old miniature log hut where the kids played cowboys and Indians. It was near another play area, and we figured at least we'd know where she was. But halfway through the game it started raining and thundering like crazy. Everybody started running for home. Brian and I were halfway there ourselves when we remembered Cathy. Brian went on home, and I went back for her.

"She was huddled inside the log house by herself, all wet and scared out of her mind. She was so scared she couldn't walk, and I had to carry her all the way home. We both got sick, and I got a tongue lashing from my father I'll never forget. I even quit the softball team, although Brian continued. I always thought Cathy eventually outgrew her fear of storms. You don't get many violent ones in Baltimore."

Travis looked hard at Chad before he relaxed. It all happened when they were kids. No one could really be blamed. And Cathy did seem to have adjusted better the last time there had been a storm. "Thunderstorms are fairly regular in Florida," Travis commented absently.

"Looks like she picked the wrong state to become a writer in," Chad said dryly.

"I disagree," Travis responded evenly, but Chad only grinned at him, knowing why he did.

They both argued good-naturedly over who would sport for the beers. Chad won. They left the restaurant and slowly headed to Travis's next departure gate. There was only one other thing he wanted to know before he left Baltimore and Cathy, especially since he was leaving without having settled a thing with her. He only had Chad's knowledge of his sister and his assurance to go on now.

"Has, ah, has Brian been to see her yet?"

"No. And he's not likely to. He's still licking his wounds and feeling very much the injured party. It's amazing how shortsighted and self-righteous he became at finding that someone else wanted Cathy. Brian has *not* been leading a life of seclusion all these years!" Chad said with wry humor.

"By the way, how is Brian's arm?" Travis asked blandly.

Chad shrugged looking at him quizzically. "Do you really care?"

"Not in the least," Travis answered tightly. "I'm only sorry now I didn't break the other one, as well!"

Chapter Fourteen

Travis thought with some surprise that nothing had changed. At least the outer buildings and property seemed the same. The enormous side yard, and the pond and the large climbable trees that had made the farm a world unto itself when he and Mitch were young remained. It had been the perfect place for two small boys, with more niches, nooks, lofts and stalls to run, jump, tumble or crawl around than they'd ever have time to explore. But they certainly had tried.

Behind the wheel of the small compact wagon, Melinda silently pretended concentration on her driving while surreptitiously noting Travis's reaction to being at the farm again. He was carefully looking all around, his brows furrowed and his mouth grimly set. One hand was a clenched fist resting on his knee. She couldn't begin to guess how he was feeling or what he might be thinking, but she recognized at least that this moment and the ones to follow were difficult ones.

Travis suddenly heard his name yelled out, and he looked out the window to see Melinda's two boys straddling a far fence, waving a wild greeting to their uncle but not yet ready to stop their activity to say hello at close quarters. With a sight smile Travis returned the wave, a sudden curling tension streaking through him. The boys might have been he and Mitch years ago, and a sensation of history repeating itself shook him.

"Sorry their welcome is long distance, but—"

Travis gave Melinda an understanding grin. "No need to apologize. They can see an uncle any old time. But how often do they get a chance to be spoiled by their grandfather?'' Travis looked out the windshield. "He does spoil them, doesn't he?"

"Outrageously so!" she said laughing. "I'm not going to be able to do a thing with them when we get back to Florida. Thank goodness school starts soon!" She swung the car off one road and onto another, seeming to circle the big white house to the front of the entrance. She saw the smile of a moment ago slowly fade from Travis's face. "I'm glad you came, Travis. It's time." Melinda spoke softly to him. Travis tensed his jaw.

"Are you glad you came, Mel?" He redirected the comment smoothly, turning to her and lifting a corner of his mouth.

"Oh, sure. The boys love it here!"

"And what about the interesting man from Boston who wanted to buy the houseboat?"

Melinda actually blushed. "He's still interesting," she said blandly. Travis continued to stare at her until Melinda relented. "Okay, okay...he's more than interesting! I like him—a lot! But we'll see. He's coming to look at the boat at the end of the month. If he buys it, it's for his parents. His father has always wanted to retire and live on a houseboat so he can sail and fish the rivers on the East Coast."

"You seem to have found out quite a bit about him. I take it he's not married?"

"Nope!" Melinda said triumphantly.

"Does he like kids?" Travis pursued softly.

"He seems to. The boys say they like him almost as much as they like you!"

"I'm not worried," Travis said easily "And I'm glad for you."

Melinda pulled the wagon up nearly in front of the door to the low ranch-style house and put the engine in neutral. "That was pretty sneaky of you," Melinda said dryly.

"What was?" Travis asked vaguely, his brow furrowing again now that they'd stopped.

"You know...not telling me how you feel about being back or about seeing Dad again."

The look Travis gave her was dark and somber. The

moment and its significance was already grabbing his attention. He quickly opened the passenger door and prepared to climb out. "Ask me at the end of the week," he commented, and swung his long body out.

Travis stood back as Melinda shifted gears and pulled the wagon away to a spot farther from the house. Travis was left standing on the slightly dusty road, looking at the house, looking off to the left, to the windows of the room that used to be his. One hand held his brown duffel; the other was thrust into the pocket of the gray slacks. Well, he was back. But he wasn't sure yet if it was still home.

His attention was caught by the opening of the door in front of him; a man of his own height struggled out, using his shoulder to hold the door while he supported his body on two hardwood canes. Two pairs of serious, searching eyes met, and the air was fairly electrified with raw emotions held tightly in check.

"So...you've come home," Jim Hoyt said in a deep gravelly voice, curiously sad and slow. They continued to stare at each other, father and son, generations apart and a sea of misunderstandings between them. But they were cut of the same cloth. Stubborn, tough and proud.

Travis's head tilted an infinitesimal degree forward. "That depends on you, I suppose."

His father watched him from icy gray eyes in a face weathered and mapped with lines but still strong. The eyes slowly softened as he shook his head at his son. "No... not me, Travis. It was always up to you. You could have come home anytime."

He turned then and struggled back into the house. Travis stood for a stunned moment, his eyes following his father's retreat. And then, letting out the tightly held and controlled breath in his lungs, Travis also went inside the house where he'd been raised.

It was to be expected that the thawing would take time. After all, four years is a long time not to have been home. There were silences to break through and awkward words and gestures. Father and son were four years different, and they had to discover how each had changed.

Travis had always seen his father as some kind of giant. As a man bigger than life, all-knowing. These youthful impressions remained intact. But Travis could also see now that his father was getting old. Despite his disability—his legs were nearly useless because of partially crushed thighbones—he got around very well. He'd adjusted. But he wasn't as strong as he used to be, either, and he tired easily now. Such a state would not be taken well by a man who'd led so vigorous and full a life as Jim Hoyt, but he didn't fight the inevitable. Sooner or later someone would have to take over the business and manage it for him.

Jim Hoyt, from his point of view, knew more about his son's past four years than he'd ever let on. It was due in part to information wrangled from Melinda. And from what Jim Hoyt could see now, he knew he could feel proud. Travis had not followed a course he himself would have chosen or even wanted for his son, but he'd done well on his own despite everything. But to Jim, Travis still seemed restless, pensive, with his attention divided.

Over a course of several days the conversation became easier, less safe and more specific, touching on old wounds that had never healed. It was to be expected, too, that Mitch's name would come up. How could it not, with so much unsettled feeling about his death between them? Travis had been all over the farm; he had gone over things that were old and familiar and those that were new. He reminisced with his father about the mischief that he and Mitch used to get into and choked with emotion to hear that his father could actually laugh gently at the memories. They got around to the business and how it had expanded. Travis learned that more sophisticated equipment and means for salvage had been added, including two small planes. Travis listened and absorbed avidly all the information and with a new interest he offered suggestions and asked questions.

Then there was the afternoon Travis quietly went off by himself for the better part of a morning, returning, if somewhat pale and quiet, much more peaceful than when he'd first arrived. Jim Hoyt, sitting in the yard in a hard straight-backed chair, watching his son come back, knew where he'd been.

Travis stopped in front of his father and eyed him sadly.

almost like the young boy he used to be when he wanted his father's understanding and approval. "I'm sorry, Dad. I never said so, but...I'm sorry about Mitch."

His father stared hard at him. "I never doubted it, son. But I never held you responsible...not once."

Travis's eyes flickered with hope. "I—I always believed you did."

Mr. Hoyt sighed. "Yes, I know. God alone knows why you did."

Travis rubbed his forehead wearily. "I don't know. We—you and I—always seemed to be at each other's throats. Every time we were together, we seemed to disagree about one thing or another."

Jim chuckled, surprising Travis again with his ability to be easy with the past. "Not *all* the time, though we certainly had our share of knock-down-drag-out fights! You had spunk and conviction.... I will give you that!"

"Probably all misplaced!" Travis said caustically as he came to sit in the grass by his father's feet and lit a cigarette.

"No, not that, either. Just different from mine. I guess I forget at times—at least I used to—how similar we are, you and I."

Travis looked at his father, then away, squinting against the late-afternoon sun, low in the sky. "Still—"

"I don't love you any more or any less than I did Mitch, Travis. I'd hoped you would always know that. Maybe it's my fault that you didn't. We were close, the three of us, in our own way. We used to be. But he was my firstborn, Travis, and I lost him. Someday, when you have sons of your own, you'll understand."

Travis's eyes immediately clouded over with a thought of Cathy. His hands clenched tightly, and his father noticed the convulsive motion. Travis didn't know what he was going to do if he couldn't see her or talk to her soon. Every night since he'd been back, he'd reached out for her in the dark, wanting to feel her next to him, missing her warmth and softness, needing so badly her love. Travis thought also about the baby and wondered painfully what would have happened between him and Cathy if she'd had the baby. Would she have let him stay? Could he have changed her mind about marrying him? Well, it was too late to change that now, but not too late to do something about the future. And he wanted one with her, even if they never had children.

Travis's father, believing his son was still dwelling remorsefully on the past, made another attempt to explain himself and inadvertently touched on the very heart of the matter for both of them. "Ah, Travis, you don't understand how it is losing a child—a son. I didn't want to lose either of you. But I'm very happy not to have lost you both that day."

The two men talked with more honesty and openness than had ever been possible before. Maybe because they were both older and had both lost so much. Maybe because they were seeing how precious time and love were in their lives.

"When you love someone, it's with your whole heart," Travis's father said to him as they got up to walk toward the pond. "And you forgive the same way."

And then Jim Hoyt looked more closely and saw past one hurt in his son's face and into another. He could see now that more than Mitchell had brought Travis back. He saw more pain and confusion and made an imperceptible move to touch him. But he held the temptation back.

"You want to tell me about it?" he asked gently in a voice raspy with age.

Travis's head came up sharply at the soft question. He searched his father's aged features and saw the man he'd always loved, the man he used to know growing up. And he saw more insight and compassion than he'd ever expected from his father before. As the two men walked slowly around the land, Travis began to tell Jim about Cathy. Not everything, of course, but enough to make it clear that he loved her deeply, wanted to build a life and home with her, and wanted the two of them to meet.

They were oblivious of the chilling air and approaching night. They sat by the trout pond until the moisture of the earth dampened their clothing, and they were stiff from sitting so long. They talked past dinner, ignoring Melinda's pealing bell. They talked past bed and on into the night until the birds reminded them of another day. And then they warily shook hands with new hope and promise. Jim clamped his hand on Travis's strong shoulder.

"Come on, son. Let's get some breakfast. I think we could both use a strong cup of coffee!"

And Travis knew he was indeed home again.

THE AUGUST SUN was delicious and warm on Cathy's limbs, baking them to a healthy brown and completely obliterating the pale gauntness she'd arrived in Baltimore with three weeks ago. Cathy licked the last of the envelopes, grimacing over the sour, sticky taste of the glue and, sealing it, added it to a waiting stack of three others.

"Well, that's that!" she murmured to herself wryly, and sat back to take a deep breath. Cathy tilted her head back against the vinyl-covered cushion of her lounge chair and closed her eyes. It was very quiet in the small yard behind the house. It was peaceful and soothing and terribly lonely. Chad had his own apartment that he'd maintained for several years, yet he'd returned to the house where he and Cathy had been raised to keep her company, sensing that she'd need it. But he had been clear and firm when he told her it was temporary. He had his own life to get back to.

Today he was in New York on a photo assignment. Tomorrow he would be in New Jersey. Cathy sighed, she might just as well have been there alone. But when Chad had told her his stay was only temporary, it was meant as a gentle reminder to his sister that she, too, would have to get on with her life.

Cathy let her head loll and roll, picking up muted sounds from neighboring yards, the summer breeze through tree leaves, birds flittering in and out of branches. So comforting and familiar, almost like it used to be at home. But not quite.

When Cathy had arrived three weeks ago, she thought she was coming back to what she'd always known. And it had been home. But there was a huge difference. *She* had changed. She had not said anything to Chad about being back, and thankfully he had not asked. Cathy had further avoided the confrontation of whys and hows by virtually sleeping the first four days away, while Chad, unknown to her, kept a brotherly vigil and a more than concerned eye on her.

She'd looked terrible when she first arrived. Much too thin and pale as death. It was obvious to Chad that she'd been sick, but again, while his mind was rampant with curiosity, he didn't ask.

By the fifth day Chad had to force her to eat, and it evoked a sweet smile from Cathy that her brother couldn't have understood. But Chad's admonishments had reminded her of Travis's forceful attitude about the care she took of herself when she was pregnant. But Cathy didn't care. For a long time she didn't care about anything. Not eating, not talking, not planning anything—not writing. There was only the persistent ache in her chest around her heart and in her very soul for Travis. She hadn't expected to miss him quite so badly. Moreover, the other thing she hadn't counted on was the hollow, abysmal, dry feeling within her body. She couldn't identify it, but it was very much like the feeling she'd had when her father died. It was infinitely sad and lonely and made her cry. Sometimes, for no apparent reason, she'd wake up in the night crying—sobbing, actually. At some point the feeling mixed with her love and need for Travis until his name was torn from her in an anguished moan. She had no idea how she was going to survive a mere week, much less the next few months—or a lifetime.

Chad had heard her in the night, and though he thought of going to comfort her, he didn't. Cathy had not come home to him for comfort. She came back because it was safe and familiar and she could hide from the real essence of her trouble. Chad now knew that to be Travis, and whatever had happened between them in Florida. Chad could love her and just be there with her—but she'd have to come to grips on her own with whatever was troubling her. And finally she had made a start.

It began the morning Cathy had gotten listlessly out of bed to make an indifferent attempt to dress for the day.

She'd tossed her nightgown on a chair and absently brushed the mop of curls out of her eyes. Cathy's head came up, and she caught a glimpse of herself in the full-length mirror attached to the back of her closet door. What she saw stilled her movements instantly. There she stood, slender and naked in the morning light of her room, and she didn't recognize herself. Her body was slender and lithe, a bit underweight, accentuating her neck and jaw, her narrow hips and small waist.

Cathy passed a hand over her flat tummy. It had always been flat. She hadn't been pregnant long enough for any real change there. Her breasts were bigger, she was sure. Cathy looked at her body now, almost as if she'd stepped out of it and could view it objectively. It was a beautifully proportioned body. Nicer than it had been a year ago, she thought with raised brows and interest. Somewhat sensual—sexy, maybe.

Then Cathy's eyes traveled to her face. It was sad, washed out, drawn. Her hair, fuller and thicker with growth, seemed to overpower her, and it made her face seem small and hidden. That had been a shock. She looked much too young. She didn't look like the person she felt herself to be—older, if not wiser, and more adult than child. A cold chill washed over Cathy as she realized what she'd been doing to herself for nearly a week. She'd been blocking out life. Refusing to live was not going to solve her worries. And if she wanted to be treated like an adult, she'd better start acting like one.

Cathy pulled open the bedroom door and poked her head out. "Chad! Chad, are you still here?" she yelled loudly into the hallway.

A moment later footsteps came bounding up the stairs, taking the creaking wood two at a time.

"Yeah, I'm here. What's the matter? Are you all right?" he asked, stopping at the landing and looking curiously at his sisters tumbled head sticking out the door.

"I'm fine. I just want to know if you have time to drop me off downtown before you leave on your assignment for the day."

Chad straightened up and the concern vanished as he

became alert to the strength and purpose in his sister's voice. "I don't have an assignment today. I can take you anywhere you like."

"Good." She withdrew her head and made to close the door.

"Cathy?"

"Yeah..."

"What do you want downtown?" There was a small pause.

"I want to get my hair cut," she said evenly, and closed the door.

For several seconds Chad stared at the closed door, and slowly a smile of surprise curved his mouth. Beginning to whistle a few meaningless chords, he went back downstairs to wait.

She was much more alert than she'd been since arriving. Not yet ready to talk but better. Cathy had not been kidding when she said she wanted to get her hair cut. It had been brutal! A near scalping. Her hair had been cut to a mere inch and a half all over, except for the front and sides, where it was only a little longer, but enough to give a soft feathery frame around her face. It brought out the lovely mature shape of her face and made her previously large eyes look more studious and disconcerting.

Chad was speechless when she came out of the shop, his mouth literally dropping at the drastic change in her appearance. But then he blinked and observed her more carefully. It worked. It brought her appearance not only up to date but up to age. It gave her presence and style, and it made her a very attractive young woman indeed.

"Well?" Cathy had asked anxiously, although her anxiety didn't show itself to Chad. He looked over his sister, liking very much what he now saw in her.

"Can I have the pleasure of taking you to lunch?" he asked with touching formality. At once Cathy recognized the compliment, a further testimony to her maturing. Her eyes misted for a second and then cleared.

"Thank you, Chad. I'd like that," she responded softly.

At lunch Chad had dared to push her a little further, encouraged by the tremendous effort she was making.

"Have you heard from Travis?" he asked with studied nonchalance, using the side of his fork to slice off a piece of fluffy omelet.

Cathy looked suspiciously at him. "I haven't said a word about Travis since I've been home. Why, for heaven's sake, are you asking about him now?"

"Precisely because you haven't," Chad said mildly, savoring his meal with exaggerated relish.

Cathy stared at him. The color had drained from her face again, but Chad knew it was too late to go back. "That doesn't mean a thing," Cathy replied quietly.

Chad decided to go for broke and really shoot all the marbles. "Come off it, Cathy," he scoffed ruefully. "I was down there, remember? I saw you two together. Are you telling me that was nothing? Brian didn't think so."

Cathy narrowed her eyes at her brother and put down her fork. For a long moment they looked at each other until Cathy gave in, dropping her eyes first. "Well, whatever it was you saw is over between us," she said coldly. The pain started all over again, and it did still hurt so.

"It wasn't the real thing, then?" he quizzed, feeling closer to the heart of the thing.

"The real thing?" Cathy repeated, and then her sable eyes grew darker—nearly black. Her mouth tightened, and she never took her eyes from those of Chad's. "I was going to have his baby!" Cathy said through clenched teeth. She blinked in horror as she realized what she'd inadvertently confessed. But there was also an odd kind of release inside her, as well, with the confession. "I—I guess that's real enough"

Chad controlled every muscle in his body. He continued to chew his food and to look at his sister with interest and attention. But he could feel his stomach sink. "I thought you couldn't," he said softly.

"So did I. I was wrong. The doctors were wrong." Picking up her iced-tea glass with an unsteady hand, Cathy took a long sip, avoiding Chad's gaze, which continued to rest on her somewhat in wonder now. Slowly, color came back to her features. "Are you surprised, shocked, disgusted?" she asked more lightly than she really felt. Chad grabbed her hand, squeezing it, and Cathy quickly held on, biting her lip. Her fingers were cold and trembling. If Chad had censured her and turned away, berated or moaned for her, she couldn't have taken it. Someone other than Elizabeth Harris and Valerie Banner *had* to understand how difficult it had all been.

"None of the above," Chad answered easily. "I could never be shocked or disgusted by you. And you haven't done anything that I can tell to be ashamed of. I take it you're no longer pregnant?" he asked quietly, for her ears only.

Cathy still couldn't meet his gaze. "No," she said shortly, not explaining, since it made no difference. Chad drew his own conclusions, however.

He looked quizzically at her. "I thought—I guess I assumed you'd naturally want to keep the baby."

Now she stared at him. "Why did you think that?"

He couldn't answer her.

"Chad, two phenomenal things happened in Florida. One was that I met Travis. And the second was that I found myself capable of bearing a child. That did not mean I was automatically prepared and capable to deal with either situation!"

Cathy then briefly explained that she had considered abortion, and she told her brother why. But she also told him that in the end the decision was not hers to make. Chad silently nodded in understanding. He dropped his voice, looking at his sister, seeing infinitely more than just physical changes in her.

"But he did come. He must have cared. It must have mattered to him."

Cathy licked her dry lips and took a deep shaky breath. "I don't know. I—I suppose now I never will."

But this couldn't be all. Chad had seen Travis and spoken to him. It wasn't over yet between them. "But what about Travis?"

This time Cathy wasn't evasive. She pulled her hand from Chad's. "I—I love him. I just don't know if we belong together anymore. If he stayed with me because of . . . the baby, then that reason is gone."

"But what does your heart tell you, Cathy? What is it you really want?"

"My heart tells me I love him. It will tell me that forever, Chad. But what I really want is to pull myself together and decide what I'm going to do. I must get back to my writing, for one thing."

"So you intend to just write about life, about love, instead of living it?"

"Maybe that's what I need to do for a while."

Chad knew that she was right. Cathy needed time and space to put the pieces back together. But Chad also knew instinctivey that Travis was one of the pieces.

Cathy suddenly looked bright-eyed at her brother. "You know that song I loved so much? 'Both Sides Now'?"

Chad relaxed as the emphasis in the conversation shifted. "How can I ever forget! I was always sorry I ever gave you the recording. I'm sure there's a deep groove worn in the disc from constant playing!"

Cathy merely smiled at his sarcastic comment. It had been her favorite song. It always would be but for different reasons now than she'd had as a teenager.

"Well? What about the song?" Chad prompted, watching the change of emotions on her face.

Cathy shrugged. "Oh, just that I really think it describes how I feel right now. About life—maybe even about love."

"You've hardly lived long enough to make snap judgments!" Chad chided her.

"But I have learned a lot. Like the song says..." Cathy quoted the words softly with meaning, her eyes watering suspiciously with tears. Chad suddenly wanted to hold and comfort her, big-brother fashion. But coddling was not what she needed. A year ago, maybe. But Cathy was a woman now, with a woman's problems and concerns.

"I don't know about it either, Cathy," he responded with a soft smile. "But welcome to the real world."

"Thanks," she whispered.

"And I honestly don't believe you've lost Travis. Maybe he just needs time, too."

Her eyes grew sad. "Chad, he hasn't even tried to reach me."

"But you haven't tried to reach him, either," he countered fairly. "Something may have come up beyond his control."

It was a reminder to Cathy that such things do happen, and had happened to her just recently.

"Cathy, sometimes you have to look hard at a person to see he's just doing the best he can." Chad held up a finger sagely and furrowed his brow in a mock-serious expression. "Remember, faith is good collateral for the person you love!"

Cathy was forced to groan and grimace playfully. "You sound like you've been reading *The Little Prince*!"

"No, it's an old proverb—taken from a Chinese fortune cookie!"

Cathy began to giggle, and Chad smiled happily at the change again. "That's much better," he said softly.

Yes, she had been much better. She didn't miss Travis any less, and the empty void continued inside. And sometimes she cried. But there were other things, too. She had gotten back to her writing, and once started, it flowed easily and quickly for hours at a time.

Keeping in mind her contract with *Miami Magazine*, Cathy wrote one of the four commissioned articles and sent it off to Valerie Banner in Florida. The second in the series she'd just finished sealing in an envelope, and it would go out that day or the next. Her poetry had picked up, and she now had a healthy stack of finished and revised verses for her book. She often found herself stopping one activity or another in order to sit and jot down prose on paper. She seemed to have so much to say and so many ideas to explore.

Some of the other letters to be mailed were letters of inquiry and proposals for a volume of her poetry. One of them was going to the publisher she used to work for—it was as good a place as any to start—and another was to a firm in New York. And finally, Cathy had written a letter to Elizabeth Harris.

CATHY WALKED AIMLESSLY around the yard, plucking a dry leaf here, pulling an overgrown weed there. There was something else on her mind. She thought she had an idea for a children's story. Or maybe it wasn't for children at all. Maybe it was for grown-ups like herself. It was a story in long verse about a special kind of box that had a dark center. And each day the center kept changing and growing until after a time it was filled with a baby, all developed and complete and much too big for the special box and ready to come into the world.

Cathy thought about the idea a lot, just as she often thought of Travis. It always made her want to cry, although for the past week she'd been controlling that urge to just give way to pure feelings and emotions. Cathy had already started the verse but had to stop writing because she seemed too close to the idea and it made her chest tight.

Cathy looked at the evidence of fall on the ground; September was only a few days away. She hadn't seen Travis in a month. It had been a month since the abortion—and the start of that strange feeling. She blinked, and as though in a trance, Cathy turned and quickly made her way into the house. She headed to her father's library and to the shelf behind his old desk where he kept the two thick family albums. Cathy's hands were shaking now, and her anxiety was making sweat break out on her forehead. She leafed quickly through the book, eyes moving rapidly, knowing exactly what she was looking for. She was sure that it had to be there, and it was.

It was a picture of her father and mother during her mother's seventh month of pregnancy with Chad. They might have been on a picnic or maybe only in the yard of that very house. But her mother, Sarah, was standing in a maternity top and skirt, looking right into the camera with a lovely soft smile on her face. Cathy's father was standing right behind her, also looking into the camera. But he wasn't smiling. It was more a look of pride and complacency. Perhaps quiet inner joy. One of his large hands was resting on his wife's shoulder. But the other was around her thickened waist, resting on the side of her rounded stomach. And one of her hands was on top of his.

Cathy stared long and hard at the picture—at her father and the look on his face. Something broke inside of her completely. Cathy suddenly understood clearly the hollow feeling inside that had been like a sore that hurt all the time. It was sorrow. It was mourning. She may have been ambivalent about the prospects of motherhood, but she had none about a baby—and she was beginning to truly feel the loss and the difference.

But it was the second realization that grabbed at her heart and settled every one of the questions she'd been asking herself since she came back to Baltimore. She felt so sure of the answer that Cathy's head came forward to rest on the glossy album page, and she began to cry as if her very heart would break—or until all of her healing was complete.

Chapter Fifteen

"The all clear was officially broadcast over four hours ago, but it had been estimated that thousands of people began returning to their coastal homes early yesterday morning. The hurricane watch, which began with the reporting last week of severe storm surges along the southern Florida tip of over twelve feet above normal sea level, has already been downgraded as the storm lost power and died out in the Gulf.

"There is a second hurricane growling out in the southern Atlantic, but it's also expected to be downgraded to a tropical storm. We're in for more rain and high winds for a few more days, but it's clear now from reports issued from the Hurricane Center at NOAA that the emergency is over.

"Although fresh water is still in short supply, electricity was finally restored at nine o'clock this evening. The continuing advisory for small crafts is that—"

Cathy switched off the radio filtering man-made sounds into the houseboat. She was left listening alertly to those of nature. The winds off Key West were a mere fifteen miles per hour compared to what had passed over north Miami and headed in a northeasterly direction during the week. The wind still angrily whipped rain against the porthole glass and washed it over the deck in erratic splashes, but it was calming down.

Cathy let out a tired sigh and got up from the built-in table of the craft to put her now-empty coffee mug in the galley. She was dressed in only the oversized red T-shirt that Travis had allotted to her ages ago and that she had donned automatically in preparation for bed. It was warm enough for just the shirt now that she'd gotten the temperamental heater working, unlike four days ago when she'd first arrived and was forced to sleep fully clothed to stay warm. As part of the routine Cathy had become accustomed to, she made sure that some of the portholes were opened to vent air. She changed the temporary caulking around the opening of the hatchway to prevent seepage of water from the upper deck. She looked once more to make sure she still had enough fresh drinking water and that the two flashlights she'd found still had working batteries. And then she stood by the partially boarded entrance to stare worriedly into the windy dark night and wonder where Travis was and if he was okay.

Cathy had gotten back to Miami as preparations were being made for the hurricane watch. And when it was clear that the predicted path would hit nowhere near Key West, Cathy had hitched rides all the way there, since no car agency would rent her a car with a storm on the horizon. It was from Joe, the bartender at the Waterfront Café that Cathy had gotten her crash course in how to protect herself and the houseboat in the storm. Since he couldn't talk her out of staying alone on the boat, he at least had checked with her to make sure she had everything for the emergency while she waited for Travis to return. And she'd been there for nearly a week.

Cathy rubbed away the slight chill that put gooseflesh on her arms as she frowned with large dark eyes into the night. She thought for sure he'd be back by now, since it was clear from the reports that for this region the storm had run its course. And each day that passed without his return or even word of him made her more afraid of what his absence could mean. For one thing, Cathy had no assurance that Travis would be returning to Key West. Joe had not seen him for several weeks, and even the houseboat, once she'd finally gotten there, had appeared dismally deserted and closed up. For another thing, what if it meant she never had a chance to tell him she loved him? It might not mean anything to Travis, but she could not do anything for herself or go on with her life until it was said.

And what if she never had an opportunity to say that for all their frailties and uncertainties they belonged to each other and she never wanted to belong to anyone else?

She had come to realize that although Travis was very special to her, he was not legendary. He was not an infallible hero of superhuman strengths or abilities. He was a man with a past and hurts and memories that he struggled with just as she did. He could be unsure of himself and frightened. He could be both frail and strong, gentle and loving, and she wanted him to love her. They had not come together under the best of circumstances, and the baby that kept them together, perhaps out of a symbiotic need, should have been conceived out of love. Even their separating seemed to have been beyond their control, their lives swept together and apart by mere chance. There had been sorrows, but it had not been a time without joy. Perhaps it could have happened better, but none of it had been bad. And in the end, if they'd both finally learned the meaning of love, then surely it had been worth it.

Surely... surely... The words echoed through Cathy's head. A wave of emotion swept over her, and tears welled up in her eyes. Surely he will come back. Surely all they'd been through together would now bring them to a new understanding. Surely they'd both had time enough to heal.

Cathy listened to a rumbling growl of thunder and watched lightning streak the sky for an instant and then disappear. *It's the other storm,* she thought absently, not for the moment recognizing the final and complete eradication of a childhood affliction. Her whole being, all her thoughts, were simply and totally involved with Travis. Feeling dispirited and on the brink of a new depression, Cathy turned out the lights and with easy familiarity made her way to the back bedroom and began dismally yet another night alone. She curled up under the blankets and listened to the rain, letting its repetitive cadence rock her to sleep.

It was still dark and still raining when Cathy heard the scraping, shuffling noise on deck. Her heart raced crazily at the initial shock of awaking and then settled to a normal rhythm in her chest. For days the wind had howled and swept loose objects and debris against the sides of the tightly moored boat. Cathy had gotten used to it, as one would the odd creaking of an old house on its foundations. But this noise was different. Cautiously and quietly, Cathy got out of bed and, reaching for the flashlight on the floor, made her way again to the front. She stopped before reaching the door, because it was once again quiet. She decided nonetheless just to take a quick look outside. There was another sound, and Cathy suddenly froze in place. The door slid open sharply, and she gasped as someone stepped in front of her. She dropped the flashlight.

There was a paralyzing silence and then "Cathy?" came an incredulous voice, for the moment disembodied. Cathy held her breath tightly, not sure that she'd actually heard her name called and almost not believing who called it.

A white beacon flashed in her face, momentarily blinding her with its brightness. She squinted painfully and automatically brought a hand up to block the glare from her eyes.

"Cat!" she heard even more distinctly, and she, too, stared in disbelief across the dark void.

"Travis!" she mouthed in a shaky voice filled with instant relief and an urge to cry. Cathy instinctively moved forward and right into Travis's arms. He had on a slicker that was all wet and very cold, and water dripped from his bare head onto her neck and back. Within seconds she was wet clear through but she didn't care and hardly noticed. Travis's rough cheek was icy against her temple, his lips frosty on her ear, but his arms closed around her in warm welcome, crushing her to him.

Travis was too shocked at having her in his arms to say anything for the time being. He just continued to hold Cathy—squeeze her, actually, as if to assure himself that she was real. There had been times as he was flying out along the Gulf and the Atlantic when he thought it was all over for him. He hadn't felt one way or another about it, except for the constant images of her and a desperate need to be with her and love her. And if he couldn't, then perhaps the end would be quick and merciful. Travis had kept her face in his mind like a talisman—a reason to get out of the storm he was in and come back. It had been good to be able to reestablish a relationship with his father, finally to know peace and forgiveness, but it was Cathy he wanted. To have actually come back to find her here now made Travis feel weak with relief.

He began to tremble and to squeeze Cathy harder, desperate to feel her against him, drawing from her body heat and proving to himself that she had survived and so had he. He held her so tightly she couldn't breathe. Her skin was chilled and shaking with the cold, and he was so completely and utterly exhausted in every sense of the word that his weight began to sag against her.

"Cathy... Travis croaked again, and dragged his mouth from her ear to her lips, leaving her cheek red and tender from the icy stiffness of his beard. Travis kissed her hard, the pressure forcing her mouth open, and at once he took possession of the area with his tongue. But his exploration was gentle and slow, further evidence of his physical state. Then, suddenly, as if all his strength and consciousness had returned, Travis grabbed Cathy by her upper arms and pushed her away from him. "What the hell are you doing here?" he exploded angrily, shaking her.

Cathy's teeth were chattering from the cold air and his voice. "I—I didn't know where you were, where you'd gone. I—I had to make sure you were all right."

"You little idiot! Don't you know you could have been hurt, even killed staying here!" He shook her again, his fingers digging painfully into the flesh of her arms.

Cathy gasped; she didn't understand why he was angry. She had worried about him so much.

But Cathy couldn't see that it wasn't anger but fright that made Travis lash out at her. He'd at least thought her safe—from himself and the weather emergency. The thought that anything further might have happened to her because of him made him wild.

"I couldn't stay away. I had to come back," Cathy whispered brokenly. Her shock caught up to her, her worry draining out of her until she was limp, and her knees felt as though they would give way. Silent tears began rolling down her cheeks, because she was so glad to see him and it was not going as she'd imagined it would.

Travis, realizing that he'd frightened her as badly as she had alarmed him, groaned and cursed softly, once again gathering her close to him. After a while he could feel her shiver. He released her and turned to close the door, moving his brown duffel out of the way. He took off the slicker, tossing it carelessly on top of the duffel. He turned on a light, which flickered for a moment but stayed. He turned back to Cathy.

Travis stared at her a moment, at once noticing the changes the past month had made. The first, of course, was her cropped hair. He felt a tugging at his heart for the cut hair, knowing instinctively that it represented a certain youthfulness that she had lost forever. But Travis loved what he saw now. There was the new slender look to her face and the maturity of her body, not the least disguised by the red T-shirt. There was much that had been stripped away from her, but what replaced the losses were beautiful to him, and he loved her all the more.

Tavis came toward her, his hand rising to stroke and finger the new hairdo while Cathy watched him anxiously. She couldn't guess what he was thinking. But she could see the bone-weary, shadowed face with its glistening beard, the stormy eyes red and clouded with exhaustion but also, for the moment, stark with wonder. His hair was wet and plastered to his scalp, hanging damply over his forehead. She watched him sway on his feet and wondered at the last time he'd gotten any decent rest. The fright he'd given her, and her worry over him, gathered and collected over several nerve-racking days, fizzled away, and she now could only think that he needed attention, love and care.

Cathy took his hand, and his strong fingers tightened convulsively as if he had no intention of letting go. She began moving backward, pulling him farther into the warm room and urging him to a chair. "I've been waiting for you," Cathy said softly as Travis eased his body into a canvas chair.

"Here?. By yourself?" he asked, bewildered, his voice and thinking weak with fatigue.

Cathy was starting to unbutton his shirt, pulling it from his pants. "Yes, here by myself," she confirmed, pushing the damp fabric over his shoulders and watching him wince from sore, overworked muscles.

Travis suddenly grabbed her wrists and stopped her movements as she reached for the bottom of the black T-shirt he also wore. "But...alone? There's been a storm raging for more than a week!"

Cathy saw the stark disbelief in his face, knowing how terrified of storms he'd seen her. Cathy gently pulled her arms free and cupped her hands lovingly on either side of his scruffy face. "I wasn't afraid for myself, Travis. I was more concerned about you. And besides, Joe has been keeping an eye on me."

Travis blinked at her, his eyes more heavy-lidded with each passing moment. Cathy's heart contracted painfully at his state, and she wanted to hold on to him, love him, take care of him and never let him go. "Cathy..." he murmured brokenly, and putting his hands on her waist drew her toward him between his spread knees and against his chest.

Cathy ran her hands into his wet hair and gratefully pressed his face into her chest. Travis's arms closed around her, his hands kneading her flesh through the T-shirt covering her thighs and buttocks. Cathy felt instinctive physical stirrings inside at the contact, but not all of it was sexual. This was where she belonged. This was where they both belonged—together. She massaged her fingers into his hair, and feeling deep emotion within herself, Cathy laid her cheek against his hair. "I love you..." she whispered, her voice barely audible. Her throat began to tighten with the uttered words, the strain of waiting so long to say them like a cork on her emotions.

Travis was still for a long moment and then with a shudder and deep groan held Cathy even tighter to him, pressing a kiss to her throat. "I love you, Cathy. Stay with me. I need you so much! Stay...please!"

"Yes—yes!" she whispered joyously.

It seemed an eternity that they held each other, perhaps afraid to let go and find it all a dream. Perhaps just needing each other as much as they did. But again Cathy began to feel Travis's weight and knew that he had to get some rest. She pulled away, prying his arms loose from around her. "Travis...look, you've got to get some sleep. I want you to go take a shower, and I'll make you something to drink. Come on now. Stand up."

Cathy had to more or less pull him to his feet. He wasn't the least interested in shower or sleep or something to drink. He just wanted to hold her. Maybe in a week he'd believe she was there and that she'd told him she loved him. For the moment, he didn't trust being away from her again. Travis began kissing her face, tasting her sweet skin with his tongue, rubbing his rough cheek against her softer one. His hands were exploring her body, riding up a side until he found a full breast, sliding down her back and up under the T-shirt to her naked back.

"Travis..." Cathy said breathlessly, wanting nothing more than to abandon herself to his touch. "Not now..."

He reluctantly released her. "You...won't go anywhere?"

"I promise," Cathy said, and watched the doubt in his face. She smiled gently at him. "My promises are a lot better than yours," she dared to tease softly. "I'll be right here when you need me."

Satisfied at least for the moment, Travis peeled off the black T-shirt, while Cathy snapped open the jeans and released the zipper. Travis sat down again to remove his boots and the rest of his clothing. Cathy hurried ahead of him to get the shower water going, while Travis followed naked behind her. Cathy stood aside and watched him step in and dunk his head under the heavy stream of water recycled from the tank. He braced his arms against the stall wall, letting the water soak his hair again and run in rivulets down his back and legs. Sure that he wasn't going to collapse, Cathy left him alone and went to make fresh coffee. She was just pouring a cup of it and lacing it with brandy when Travis emerged from the shower, one towel around his middle and another around his shoulders.

Cathy finished her preparations, turned off the lights and led Travis to the bedroom. While he sat heavily on the edge of the bed with the steaming cup, Cathy crawled behind him; kneeling, she brisky towel-dried his hair.

"Did you fly during the storm?" Cathy asked as she worked.

"Right into the eye of it," Travis mumbled drowsily.

"Was it...dangerous?"

"I suppose," Travis said after a moment. "I didn't really think about it. I...didn't really care."

Her hands faltered. "Why? Why didn't you care?" she asked thinly. She could feel him sigh, feel his shoulders hunch forward.

"I'd already lost so much...it didn't matter. I thought I'd lost you."

Cathy stopped rubbing his hair and sat back on her heels. She didn't know how to tell him yet that she knew what he was feeling, that her heart had ached when she had recognized her own feelings. Cathy realized that she'd also been blind. She'd never considered Travis's feelings, never thought that he'd have any concerning the baby. She'd locked him out of her decision and rejected sympathy, understanding and maybe even his love.

"I was going to come for you, Cathy," Travis said in a tired voice. "As soon as this was over, I was going to come...no matter what Chad said."

Cathy moved so that she was sitting almost next to him, her legs tucked under and to the side of her body. "Chad?" she asked blankly. "What does he have to do with this?"

Travis looked at her, then back to the cup in his hands. He let out another sigh. "I came to Baltimore after you'd left Miami. Elizabeth Harris guessed you might be there. I saw Chad. He met me at the airport. We talked. He said you needed time."

Cathy smiled gently at him, touching the hard muscles of the arm in front of her. "I needed to go home for a while. But Chad never said he spoke to you."

"I'm glad he didn't. What I wanted you to know only I should tell you."

"Like...what?"

Travis put the cup down and turned partially to her. He put an arm across her lap and braced it on the bed so that Cathy was facing him and within the half circle of his arm. "I didn't stay with you just because of our baby...but because I needed you."

Cathy was alert to his term "our" baby, and her heart began to race, color flaming her face.

"Some things have changed, but I still need you and love you."

"Oh, Travis..." Cathy said brokenly around the start of tears she knew would have to come. Travis brought his arm completely around her and pulled Cathy onto his lap.

"I went home to see my father," Travis murmured into her hair, holding and rocking her gently. "We still love and care for each other."

"I always knew that was so. I'm happy for you," Cathy whispered, a tear rolling down her cheek. "I'm glad that everything...is all right now."

Travis smiled and rubbed his thumb over her chin. "Not yet...but almost." Cathy raised her teary eyes, and he was just a blur. "I didn't know if I had your love and forgiveness. I wasn't sure I ever would. But I told my father if I ever found out, I'd bring you home with me to Boston.

"You wouldn't marry me just because of the baby, and I loved you even then." His voice was low and emotionally charged, the words spoken with difficulty.

"Travis...I..." Cathy began, but Travis squeezed her and interrupted.

"Do you love me?" he asked. Cathy merely nodded, biting her lip against the flow of her tears. "Will you marry me now?" Again she nodded. "Then that's all that matters." Then he bent to give her the gentlest kiss, his lips barely touching the cool surface of hers. But his eyes were curiously hollow, still hiding something from her.

Travis swung her to the floor and began pulling the covers back over the bed. He discarded the second towel and reached to pull Cathy's T-shirt over her head, leaving her also naked. He held up the linens until she'd climbed into the bed. Then, turning out the wall light, he, too, got in beside her.

Cathy knew it was not finished, and despite her love for Travis and his for her, the hardest words were yet to be said. But she couldn't. She didn't know how. Instead, she cried silently, helplessly, while Travis held her in his arms and felt her body quake. The distinct pressure of her nipples against him and the feel of her slender bare thighs were erotically pleasing—but also comfortingly familiar. He held her closer, and some of his control began to give way as he listened to her crying. He stroked a silky thigh.

"Don't cry, Cat. Please don't. It's going to be okay."

"I'm...sorry! Oh, Travis...I'm so sorry. I didn't know—I—I never realized!"

Travis swallowed hard and pressed her head into his shoulder, smoothing his hand over her short curls, or what was left of them—so much lost. "Don't talk, sweetheart."

"Travis, I didn't think you wanted the—the baby. I didn't realize you really cared!" Her body shook.

Travis shuddered. "Cat..."

"Forgive me! I—I'm so sorry."

"Oh, God!" Travis moaned, clenching his teeth, and it wasn't going to help.

Cathy went suddenly stiff in his arms. "The baby! I never asked. I don't even—" Cathy stopped talking as Travis buried his face in her neck and his arms and hands became tight on her as he held on.

"It was...a boy," he croaked. Cathy held her breath. For a moment she even stopped crying, but the shock overcame her again, and finally even Travis let go of his feelings. "A boy," he repeated.

They locked themselves into each other's arms and each other's sorrow...and together cried out their pain.

CATHY STOOD ON THE DECK, the wind ruffling her disordered hair. Already it was growing back, but she knew she would never let it get as full and curly as it had been before. Travis had approved of the decision by saying the shorter cut made her sexier. He had punctuated that remark with a thorough kiss and a brief suggestive squeeze to her bottom.

It was three days after the predicted second storm and four days since Travis had returned to her. The sky was clearing, and the squall lines were so far away that whatever minor storm might be working its way into a frenzy was never going to reach land before nightfall. Cathy took a deep breath of the salty sea air; she'd always associated its peculiar smell with Key West. She was not going to miss it there, or Florida, once they started for Boston. They were packing Travis's things now, but there was going to be a multitude of memories. She had found Travis there, and love. And she had grown up there.

She considered all the things that she still had to remove from the Miami apartment, and she was hoping to meet with Valerie Banner. When she'd phoned Chad the day before, she'd learned that there was an interested response to her proposal on the book of verse from the New York publisher. Everything was falling into place....

"Cat?"

The door slid open behind Cathy, and Travis stepped out, coming up behind her to slip his arms around her waist and interlock his fingers over her stomach. He kissed her cheek. "What are you doing out here? Can't you see it's going to rain?"

"Not for a few more hours yet." Cathy smiled, tilting her head to his warm mouth.

Travis squeezed and chuckled. "What...have you become a sage or something. Just remember I'm the weather expert in this family!" Cathy only smiled peacefully. Travis settled her back against his chest and rested his chin atop her head. "What are you thinking?"

Cathy look wistfully out over the key and sighed. "I was thinking that if I ever have a little girl, I'll call her...Jenny Rebecca."

Travis's eyes crinkled at the corners in amused indulgence. "Sounds like the name of someone's grandmother."

Cathy, undaunted by his sarcasm, grimaced prettily up at him. "Don't laugh! It's a beautiful name."

"It is," Travis conceded, ruffling her hair and pulling a short curl. "And very romantic."

"And it's also a beautiful song."

"No doubt," Travis continued, watching the breeze stir a rosy color into her cheeks.

"If you had a daughter, what would you call her?" Cathy asked, expecting that his lack of imagination would cause him to shrug indifferently and say he hadn't given it a thought.

Travis turned her around, his eyes traveling over her pert upturned face, the square jaw with more determination than anyone had ever given her credit for. "Katherine—with a K," he announced, seeing the widening surprise in Cathy's eyes. "And I'd call her Kate for short." Cathy was speechless at the implied compliment. "But it's a purely academic question, since we've already decided to wait a year or two. Right?"

"Right," Cathy agreed, putting her arms around his neck. "But there's no harm in being prepared, is there?"

Travis searched her pretty face. "None whatsoever. But I can think of another way to do it," and he began moving back into the houseboat, pulling Cathy with him as he bent to playfully nip, lick and kiss her mouth.

"Travis!" Cathy feigned complaint. "We practiced and prepared all last night!"

He kissed her complaint away, eliciting a soft moan in its place as his tongue gently invaded her open mouth and then released her. "Practice makes perfect!" he countered with a wicked grin, and then gathering her to him, kissed her in earnest, a kiss and caress that was not a tease but that clearly stated how much he loved her. His hands moved to her buttocks and, curving around her bottom, pulled her into his already-aroused hard middle.

"Umm...your practice is killing me," Cathy crooned softly, not a word of truth in her reply.

Travis laughed softly. "We might as well now. When I get you to Boston, we'll be too busy getting settled."

She pulled back to look at Travis seriously. "Travis, are you sure your father won't mind? I mean, if it's going to be too crowded, maybe we should find our own place."

Travis hid his amusement, still wanting to surprise Cathy with the fact that his father's crowded place was a thirteen-room house with nearly two hundred acres of land around it. He brushed his mouth lightly over hers. "I'm sure Dad won't mind."

Travis leaned back against the edge of the built-in dining table and pulled her between his outstretched legs. Cathy pressed into his lean body with sensual familiarity.

"I think Chad would like us to stop by and visit with him for a few days. I think he should get to know you."

"Did you two talk about me behind my back?" Travis asked with a raised brow.

Cathy grinned, flushing a little as she stroked his jaw and cheek. "A little. I told him all the good things I loved about you."

Travis chuckled dryly, his hand smoothing over her lower back and hips. "Oh? That must have taken about ten seconds."

Cathy giggled, and Travis regarded her amusement with loving warm eyes. He kissed the end of her nose. "And did you tell him all my bad points, as well?"

Cathy wrinkled her nose. "There were only a few," she said. Travis watched her reticence in voicing them, and he placed a hand under her chin, lifting her face.

"Well?" he asked.

Cathy dropped her lashes, veiling her chocolate-colored eyes. "I—I told him you don't know how to be happy and you're much too hard on yourself. And I said you can be very stubborn, and you smoke too much!" Cathy looked at him now, her eyes seductive and soft. "I also told him that despite all your shortcomings I was very much in love with you."

Travis swallowed, his fingers gently exploring her face. He could think of nothing to say in the face of a declaration that left him so moved. "And what did Chad say to all of that?"

Cathy shrugged. "He said you sounded reasonably sane and to bring you home!"

Travis suddenly laughed in his deep voice, real amusement softening his angular features. "Is he planning on meeting us with a shotgun in hand?"

"Chad isn't like that!" Cathy said indignantly.

Travis kissed her briefly and hugged her to him. "It doesn't matter. I plan to make you an honest woman before we visit." Cathy snuggled happily in his embrace. "Cathy... You were right, you know."

"About what?" she asked absently, enjoying Travis's kissing and caressing.

"You do see things clearly when you use your heart."

Cathy opened her eyes and smiled at him. "I told you so," she said, coming up on tiptoe to reach his mouth with her own. "And just think. We have a lifetime to work on perfect vision!"

ARLEQUIN *Love Affair*

Now on sale

ONLY WITH THE HEART   *Sandra Kitt*

Travis Hoyt emerged from the night to pluck her from a rain-swept doorway. His manner was rough, his face forbidding, but Cathy Donnelly gratefully accepted his offer of sanctuary from the storm. Soaked to the skin, chilled to the very marrow of her bones, Cathy followed Travis across a deserted Key West dock, too tired for second thoughts and much too young to be afraid.

It was to be an unforgettable night for them both. . . .

THE STORM WITHIN   *Anne Henry*

Sally Jo Hampton had borne all kinds of indignities as Sally Storm, Oklahoma City's most popular weathergirl. But when the station manager decided to change her image from simpering to sultry, Sally realized it was time to find a job that recognized her professional merits instead of her face and figure. Her search led her to the National Tornado Project and Dr. Neal Parker.

Neal disliked her reporting style, yet he always watched her broadcasts. Sally had to convince him of her intellectual capabilities. In fact, in her struggle to make him understand the real Sally Hampton, that was only the beginning.

HIDING PLACES   *Modean Moon*

The only truth in Hillary Michaels's life had been her love for Anton Roeffler. But Anton would never believe that—how could he? When she had arrived in Altus, Arkansas, four years ago, Hillary had exchanged her name for a pseudonym and invented a placid history for herself that had nothing to do with fact. She had known a few months of peace, until the past—and the truth —caught up with her.

Now Hillary returned to Altus not to explain herself to Anton —she knew that was futile—but to reason with him before their lies and deceptions ruined someone else's life.

HARLEQUIN *Love Affair*

Next month's titles

CHANGING PLACES   *Beverly Sommers*

What do you get when you cross a New York city slicker with a beer-drinking, pool-shooting good old boy? The citizens of Rock Ridge, Georgia, couldn't rightly tell, what with all the fur flying. The hostilities commenced about the time Carol Jones tried to buy Raney Catlin a drink—as though any self-respecting man would let a woman pay his way!

But Carol didn't understand the ways of country folk. She had only exchanged her New York apartment with the occupant of the quaint mountain cabin for six months. How could she learn the Rock Ridge way in so short a time? Worse yet, how could she learn to deal with Raney Catlin?

LOVERS NEVER LOSE   *Muriel Jensen*

Dana MacKenzie hoped for a challenging job at the weekly paper in Warrenton, Oregon. What she got was chaos and uproar. The office was managed by a smart-mouthed teenager who squeezed in work hours between her high-school classes. Local news was culled from the gossipy reports of an obstreperous little old lady. And the publisher, Gabe Cameron, just barely managed to get the paper printed by antique machinery that constantly threatened collapse.

These certainly weren't the surroundings Dana was accustomed to. But then again, Gabe, with his frenetic pace and outrageous friends, wasn't like any man she had ever met.

AN UNEXPECTED GIFT   *Andrea Davidson*

Despite his charm, Greg Fisher was a fool. To have wagered his career, his reputation and most probably his life against the possibility of finding a legendary mine! Oh, Anne knew he thought no better of her, a silent, suspicious biologist who clambered about in the Rockies peering at a herd of sheep. It was obvious Greg thought she was crazy.

Normally, Anne wouldn't have had anything to do with him. But with his brand-new camping gear and his ridiculous cache of candy bars, he was also a menace. She couldn't allow him to blunder through the wilderness alone. He didn't know how vast it was—or how dangerous.